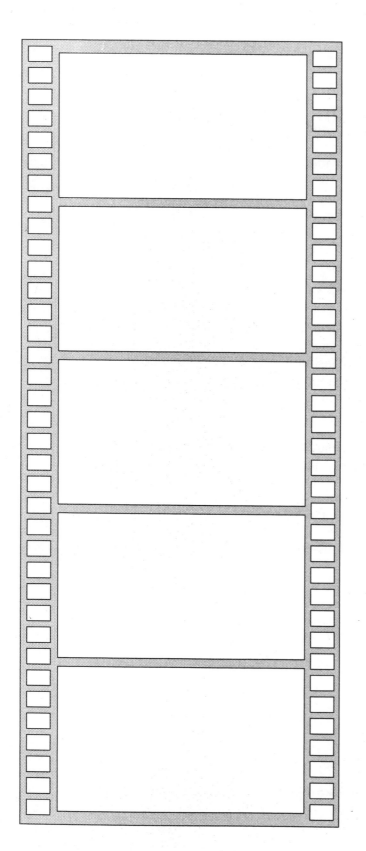

To Kill a Mockingbird and 24 More Videos

Language Arts

Activities

for Middle School

Randy Larson

J. Weston Walch, Publisher
Portland, Maine

Users' Guide
to
Walch Reproducible Books

As part of our general effort to provide educational materials which are as practical and economical as possible, we have designated this publication a "reproducible book." The designation means that purchase of the book includes purchase of the right to limited reproduction of all pages on which this symbol appears:

Here is the basic Walch policy: We grant to individual purchasers of this book the right to make sufficient copies of reproducible pages for use by all students of a single teacher. This permission is limited to a single teacher, and does not apply to entire schools or school systems, so institutions purchasing the book should pass the permission on to a single teacher. Copying of the book or its parts for resale is prohibited.

Any questions regarding this policy or requests to purchase further reproduction rights should be addressed to:

Permissions Editor
J. Weston Walch, Publisher
P.O. Box 658
Portland, ME 04104-0658

—J. Weston Walch, Publisher

1   2   3   4   5   6   7   8   9   10

ISBN 0-8251-2304-6

— Contents —

— To the Teacher —

I remember sitting in science class in junior high and getting excited as the lights dimmed and the movie projector began to chatter. A grandfatherly scientist from Bell Laboratories loomed large on the three-legged screen and began to tell about the neat workings of our universe and the role that the sun played in it all. When it was over, someone snapped on the light, shut off the projector, and totally shattered the dream. I remember looking around, while I collected my books, at all the sad and lonely friends of Mr. Sun who had to get ready for Phys. Ed. within a few minutes of the next bell. It was a shock that I felt deeply, and could do nothing about—until now.

I've written this book because I've learned that shutting off a video machine doesn't shut off the emotions and imaginings of the audience, and that the best opportunity for teaching is right after the words THE END appear; it's where real learning can start, if we know how to seize the moment. The activities included in this text give you some effective ways to move kids from the world they've encountered on film to the realities of curriculum requirements in the classroom. I've included essays, projects, speeches, interviews, self-studies, word games, multiple choice and true/false quizzes, vocabulary and spelling exercises, and more, in order to bring variety to the task of learning from film. By using the teaching tips listed on the following page, and by selecting exercises appropriate to students of various ability levels, you can help create a meaningful experience for every student.

There are many good English teachers who resist this experience out of hand. Their position is that too much time is already spent by today's youth in front of a television screen. Why provide even more viewing time in school? For those earnest souls I offer the following evidence on behalf of video use in the English/Language Arts classroom:

- First—Let's be practical. Videos are cheap. A classroom set of novels might run $90–$180, while a video costs $2–$4 to rent. If you're short of funds, videos are one answer.

- Second—Videos are time-savers. You can show a video in three days, while a novel may take three weeks. In a packed curriculum, videos allow time to teach more skills at a greater depth.

- Third—Videos provide a springboard into all sorts of other genres and media—poetry, plays, essays, biographies, novels, screenplays, research, and journalism. After a video many students ask for more; I immediately suggest a book, a poem, an essay, or a news feature that expands on the topic or relates to the film in some important way.

- Fourth—Videos are democratic in their range and depth. All students can get to the core of most films, not just the literati who are sensitive to the rhythm and nuance of language. This makes for more inclusive class discussions, and more success on written assignments.

- Fifth—Videos provide variety. In a curriculum that looks dolefully out upon 180 days of school, one must reach for new ways to teach kids. Videos can be a handy solution to the doldrums.

- Finally—Videos are powerful expressions of great artists' and directors' visions. They bring a dimension to a piece of literature that cannot be found on the stage or in a book. Since it is an English teacher's task to make as many literary experiences available to kids as possible, videos should be used in the classroom whenever the opportunity strikes.

And there's one more reason for teaching literature through videos—this book. The many activities within its covers give you a wide range of exercises to offer students in this engaging approach to the study of literature. It is my hope that by using this text, my colleagues will be better able to give students what can be rightfully called a good education.

— Teaching Tips —

Preview, Preview, Preview

The films in this book were chosen to include a wide range of interests, abilities, and school climates. Some contain nudity (*Romeo and Juliet*) while others have some profanity in them (*When the Legends Die, West Side Story, Raisin in the Sun,* et al.) while still others contain suggestive scenes (*Fahrenheit 451*) that you may not want your students to see. *Preview* each film before showing, to determine whether the film is appropriate for your classes.

Choose Wisely

Finding the right film for the right group of students is critical. If the film is too complex for sixth graders (*Raisin in the Sun*, for example), you could spend more time stopping horseplay than anything else. If the video is too simplistic for, say, an advanced group of freshmen, boredom wins out and the exercise is a disaster. The best way to solve this problem is to imagine the average student from a particular class watching the film with you as you preview it. Try to internalize his or her reaction to the dialogue, action (or lack of it), theme, and tone of the film.

Prepare The Way

Read the plot summary provided here, then preview the film and make a few notes about key points or scenes that you want the students to notice. Bypass the credits and start the tape with the action. Set the tape counter to zero and keep track of where you finish for that day on a 3 x 5 card for each class. Set the VCR in a convenient place for optimum viewing by all students, preferably up on a stand or cart at the front of the room.

Stop Often—Lights On!

Pause the film whenever you need to make a brief, important point, and turn the lights on if you feel it will help the students focus their attention. In fact, some teachers keep the lights on during the entire film. Have short discussions as the movie progresses. Even a short quiz would work in some cases.

Quit Early

Try not to end a tape when the bell rings. Shutting things down about 10–15 minutes before class ends gives you a chance to hold a brief discussion on one or two major points in the film. Letting the kids drift out the door as the bell rings gives them 24 hours to forget what they saw.

Make a Viewing Guide

Jot down some key points and questions about scenes from the film on slips of paper and photocopy them for the students' reference as the tape rolls. They will be more apt to stay "on task" if they have to respond, even if briefly in one-word answers, to some short, to-the-point questions.

Subscribe

One of the best publication aids for teachers using video in their classes is *Learning Enrichment*, published by Learning Enrichment, Inc., Grand Central Station, P.O. Box 5530, New York, N.Y. 10163-5530. This newsletter/magazine gives tips on how to use television and video more effectively in the classroom; explains the "fair use" laws for teachers who want to tape certain programs off the major networks for use in the classroom; and lists "coming attractions" (movies, series, news programs, specials) that might appeal to teachers of all disciplines.

1. TO KILL A MOCKINGBIRD

Author: Harper Lee
Novel Title: *To Kill a Mockingbird*
Director: Robert Mulligan

Running Time: 131 minutes
Year: 1962
Format: black and white

Summary

Atticus Finch is a middle-aged, widowed lawyer raising two children in the small town of Maycomb, Alabama, in 1932. He is a man of great integrity who can't quite keep up with the energies of his six-year-old daughter, Scout (Jean Louise), who is about to start school. Jem, Atticus' eleven-year-old son, wants a gun, but Atticus won't let him have one and warns Jem about shooting innocent mockingbirds.

The film is narrated by Scout, who is looking back on a dramatic time in her childhood that began when she and her brother met a boy named Dill, who was visiting for the summer from Meridian, Mississippi. He dares them into trying to get the mysterious character named Boo Radley (Arthur Radley) to come out of his house, where he's been kept since he was a teenager. Legends abound: Boo is tall, fierce, and bloodthirsty. The children run up on the porch, or peek in the windows, or slap the side of the house and run off. It's all a great, dangerous game.

But the frivolous nature of things diminishes as Jem keeps finding small gifts in the hollow of a tree outside of the Finch home: a pocket knife, spelling medals, carved dolls, and bits of chewing gum. Boo is trying to communicate with Jem and Scout, trying to touch some human life outside of his dark, stifling world.

In the midst of this, Atticus is caught up in the trial of Tom Robinson, a black man accused of raping a white woman, MayElla Ewell. Her father, Bob Ewell, is a violent, poor, ignorant man who is clearly racist in his mind, and wicked at heart. He testifies that he caught Tom with his daughter and chased him off. But Atticus proves that MayElla's bruises and wounds were administered by someone who was left-handed (Bob Ewell). Tom Robinson lost the use of his left arm in a farm accident when he was a child. But Tom is found guilty anyway, and on his way to being transported to another jail, is killed by a deputy who said Tom tried to run away.

The shock of Tom's death puts an end to any childish behavior on Jem's and Scout's part until Halloween, when they attend a costume party. Scout, who has lost her dress, must walk home ensconced in a papier-mâché ham costume. On the way home she and Jem are frightened by noises and then attacked by someone they can't identify. Jem's arm is broken and he's knocked unconscious, then the attacker goes for Scout. Before he can touch her, another figure appears, stabs Bob Ewell with his own kitchen knife, and carries Jem off into the night to the Finch's home, where Atticus immediately calls the doctor and Sheriff Heck Tate.

Sheriff Tate asks Jean Louise if she can tell him who carried Jem home and she points to a shadowed corner of the room, where Boo (Arthur) Radley is standing. "That's him, Mr. Tate," she says, and then says, "Hey, Boo." "Meet Mr. Arthur Radley," Atticus says, and instantly all the mystery and illusion vanish. Scout takes Boo's hand and they walk out onto the porch.

Atticus and Heck Tate are discussing what to do. "You don't think Jem killed Bob Ewell, do you, Mr. Finch?" Heck says. Both men look at Boo. "A black man's dead for no reason and now the man responsible for it is dead. Let the dead bury the dead this time, Mr. Finch," Heck pleads. "I ain't much, but I'm still the Sheriff of Maycomb County, and I say Bob Ewell *fell* on his knife."

Atticus is stunned and confused. Scout says, "Atticus, Mr. Tate is right. It would be like shooting a mockingbird, wouldn't it?" Atticus thanks Boo for saving his children, then Scout walks him home, stands on his porch, and in a moment of revelation, understands and knows Boo in a way she never thought possible. She goes back home and waits in Jem's room with Atticus.

Name _____ Date _____

1. To Kill a Mockingbird

Plot Sequence

The plot of a book or movie is made up of the events that happen to the characters. If the events are interesting and challenging to the characters, then the story will probably be interesting to the reader/audience as well.

Below are some of the events that make up the plot of the film *To Kill a Mockingbird*. Number the events according to which happened first, which happened second, third, fourth, and so on. Numbers one, two, and three are done for you.

1. _____ Jem's arm is broken.

2. _____ Boo is standing behind the door of Jem's room.

3. ___1___ Jem is sitting in his tree house refusing to come down until Atticus agrees to play football for the Methodists.

4. ___2___ Mr. Cunningham delivers a bag of nuts to Atticus in payment for legal services.

5. ___3___ Dill introduces himself as Charles Baker Harris.

6. _____ Scout puts on a dress for school.

7. _____ Scout takes Boo home.

8. _____ Scout meets Boo face to face.

9. _____ Jem almost gets shot in Mr. Radley's garden.

10. _____ Tom Robinson testifies at his own trial.

11. _____ Tom is convicted of attacking MayElla Ewell.

12. _____ Tom is shot to death.

13. _____ The entire courtroom stands as Atticus walks out.

14. _____ Heck Tate decides not to arrest Boo because it would be like killing a mockingbird, which is a sin.

15. _____ Atticus tells Tom's wife that Tom has been killed.

1. To Kill a Mockingbird

Homonyms

Homonyms are words that sound the same but are spelled differently:

> piece—peace
> principal—principle
> break—brake
> alter—altar

Circle the correct word from the pair of homonyms in each sentence below.

Example: Jem (lead, led) the way through the crowd to the front, where Atticus stood.

1. Tom Robinson testified that MayElla Ewell had said, "Come (hear, here), boy, and bust up this chifforobe for me."

2. When the verdict was given it seemed that Tom was almost too stunned to really (here, hear).

3. Jem was (already, all ready) home when Scout arrived to tell Atticus about being attacked.

4. When Scout got up to prepare for school, her breakfast was (all ready, already).

5. Atticus knew that telling Tom's wife about her husband's death would (brake, break) her heart.

6. Scout probably wished that the tire she was riding in had a (brake, break) on it.

7. Every day Mr. Radley walked (to, too, two) the store.

8. Calpurnia served (plane, plain) but hearty meals every day.

9. The (principal, principle) reason that Atticus defended Tom was that he believed "All men are created equal."

10. The children tried (their, there) best to help Atticus when he was in trouble.

Name _____ Date _____

1. To Kill a Mockingbird

Vocabulary

The courtroom scene is an important event in the story. To better understand it you should know some basic information about the legal process. Look up the terms listed below and write their definitions on the lines provided.

Compare your answers with three or four classmates, and discuss any differences with your teacher.

1. jury: _____

2. bailiff: _____

3. court stenographer: _____

4. defending attorney: _____

   _____

5. prosecuting attorney: _____

   _____

6. judge: _____

7. indictment: _____

8. sentence: _____

9. due process of law: _____

   _____

10. self-incrimination: _____

    _____

11. testimony: _____

12. evidence: _____

    _____

Name _____ Date _____

1. To Kill a Mockingbird

Letter

Tom Robinson is held in jail, behind bars like a bird in a cage. He believes he is doomed, that he will be killed by white racists who have imprisoned him wrongly.

What would he say in a final letter to his wife and family?

Write a letter from Tom as he thinks over his life and considers all the people he's known and loved over the years. What are his regrets? How angry at society is he? What are his feelings about the conditions of black people in the South?

Dear Helen,

_____

_____

_____

_____

_____

_____

_____

_____

_____

_____

_____

_____

_____

1. To Kill a Mockingbird

Answers

Plot Sequence

1.	11	4.	2	7.	15	10.	6	13.	8
2.	12	5.	3	8.	13	11.	7	14.	14
3.	1	6.	4	9.	5	12.	9	15.	10

Homonyms

1. here
2. hear
3. already
4. all ready
5. break
6. brake
7. to
8. plain
9. principal
10. their

Vocabulary

1. jury: people who hear a case in court and render a decision
2. bailiff: a person who keeps order in the court
3. court stenographer: a person who records all that is said in the courtroom
4. defending attorney: a lawyer who prepares a case for the person accused
5. prosecuting attorney: a lawyer who brings a case against someone in a court of law
6. judge: a person who hears a case and makes decisions in a court of law
7. indict: to charge with a crime
8. sentence: the punishment for a crime
9. due process of law: the required procedure for arresting, charging, and trying a person in a court of law. Due process is guaranteed to all citizens.
10. self-incrimination: testimony against oneself
11. testimony: statements made under oath to establish facts
12. evidence: a statement or object bearing on a point in question in a court of law

Letter

Answers will vary.

2. SOUNDER

Author: William Armstrong
Novel Title: *Sounder*
Director: Martin Ritt

Running Time: 105 minutes
Year: 1972
Format: color

Summary

Nathan Morgan, a black man living in Louisiana during the Depression, finds the misery of feeding his family overwhelming, and steals meat from a nearby farm. He is arrested, and while he's being taken into custody, one of the officers shoots and severely wounds Sounder, the Morgans' trusted hound. The dog runs off to heal himself in the woods. Nathan is taken to a labor camp to serve a one-year sentence.

The sheriff won't tell any blacks the prison location of any of their kin, but David, Nathan's oldest child, is determined to find his father. He enlists the help of a white woman, Mrs. Boatwright, who agrees to see the sheriff of Landsburg Parish and ask for information about Nathan Morgan. She is rebuked, but she sneaks into the files and finds the name of the camp where Nathan is being held. She refuses to give the name to David at first, having been threatened by Sheriff Young. But later Mrs. Boatwright appears at the Morgan cabin with a map and the name they need: Wishbone Labor Camp in Nolantown.

David begins his journey, taking his dog, Sounder, and some food. He spends many days on the road and finally comes upon the camp, where striped-suited prisoners are at work. He inquires but is beaten off by the guard. He runs off, his hand bleeding from the guard's blows, and continues the search for his father, to no avail.

David does find a friend—a schoolteacher named Camille Johnson who takes him in, cleans his bloodied hand, feeds him, encourages him, and puts him up for the night. Then she sends David on his way with a plan—the boy is to go home and return in the fall to live with Miss Johnson and attend her school.

David returns home and helps with the harvest. The weeks and months pass, then one day Rebecca hears Sounder growling and looking down the lane. It is Nathan, hobbling along with a crutch as he makes his way toward the house. He has been hurt in a dynamite blast and the authorities have released him ". . . after I was no more use to 'em," Nathan said.

David is so afraid to separate himself from his father that he refuses to attend Miss Johnson's school; he wants to help with the work while his father's leg heals. Nathan demands that David go. David resists. The two argue and David runs off.

Nathan follows David and finds him sitting on a log by the river. He tells the boy how he beat death in the quarry when the dynamite exploded and he tells David to ". . . beat the life they got all laid out for you in this place." David hears what his father is saying. He knows that Nathan is right and that an education is the only way out of the poverty and prejudice. In this powerful scene, Nathan says to David, "Are we ever gonna get to be friends?"

In the final scene, David is traveling in a buckboard wagon with his father toward Miss Johnson's school. David says, "I'm going to miss this ol' raggedy place, but I sure ain't gonna worry about it."

2. Sounder

True or False

Mark the true statements below with a plus (+) sign, and mark the false statements with a zero (0). If the statement is false, explain *why* it is false on the lines provided.

1. ___ Nathan Morgan stole meat from a nearby farmer's smokehouse because he was envious of the man's prosperity.

   _____

2. ___ Nathan Morgan never discusses the "right or wrong" of his crime with David, his son.

   _____

3. ___ Sounder, the hunting dog, never really plays much of a role in the movie.

   _____

4. ___ Because David is slow in school, he has to hire out to Camille Johnson as a handyman.

   _____

5. ___ David shows his love for his father by traveling many miles to find him and bring news from the family.

   _____

6. ___ The sheriff won't tell Mrs. Morgan where her husband is because Nathan's crime is too serious to allow visitors.

   _____

7. ___ Mrs. Boatwright turns out to be cowardly and betrays the Morgan family.

   _____

8. ___ Nathan comes home exactly one year later, after he has served his time.

   _____

9. ___ Nathan sends his son away because he realizes they will never see eye to eye on how to live in a racist society.

   _____

10. ___ The movie ends on a note of despair as Nathan and David ride off together.

   _____

2. Sounder

Prepositions

Prepositions are powerful words that are pretty much ignored in most sentences because they're so common. They include *at, by, for, in, of, on, to, up,* and several dozen others that are taken for granted. These simple words explain the relationship between the nouns or pronouns attached to them, and other words in a sentence.

     Example: The drugs were found *near* the car.
                    The drugs were found *in* the car.

Which preposition is more likely to get someone arrested?

Here is a list of commonly used prepositions:

about, above, across, after, against, along, amid, among, around, at, before, behind, below, beneath, beside, between, beyond, by, down, during, except, for, from, in, into, like, near, of, off, on, over, past, since, through, throughout, to, toward, under, underneath, until, unto, up, upon, with, within, without

Read the paragraph below and list twenty-five prepositions found in it on the lines provided. (You may list the same preposition more than once.)

The relationship between David and his father was one of the main themes in the movie Sounder. *Nathan Morgan expected a lot from his oldest son; the boy was supposed to help on the farm, keep pace with his schoolwork, and hunt all night to provide food for the family. By working side by side, David and Nathan grew close, sometimes close enough to cause friction between them, like rubbing two rocks together. At the opening of the film when Nathan misses the raccoon and criticizes Sounder, David teases his father about being beaten by the raccoon. Nathan snaps at his son because he is hurt and angry that he couldn't provide meat for the family. Throughout the film the boy and Nathan Morgan exchange words that no one else in the family hears. They have a special relationship that only grows stronger as they go through the difficult struggle of surviving in a racially prejudiced society.*

1. _____   6. _____   11. _____   16. _____   21. _____

2. _____   7. _____   12. _____   17. _____   22. _____

3. _____   8. _____   13. _____   18. _____   23. _____

4. _____   9. _____   14. _____   19. _____   24. _____

5. _____   10. _____   15. _____   20. _____   25. _____

2. Sounder

Prepositional Phrases

Below is a list of prepositional phrases. Write ten sentences based on the movie *Sounder*, using each phrase once in each sentence. You may use other phrases to help make your sentences work, but be sure to include those on the list below. Circle the prepositional phrase in each sentence.

Example: Sounder liked to hunt (beneath a shining white moon.)

Prepositional Phrases:

from books	for his mother
in his father	about Sounder
behind him	at school
with the chores	within his heart
along the road	to the prison camp

1. _____

2. _____

3. _____

4. _____

5. _____

6. _____

7. _____

8. _____

9. _____

10. _____

2. Sounder

Adverb Phrases and Clauses

An adverb phrase is a prepositional phrase that modifies a verb, adjective, or another adverb. An adverb clause has a subject and a verb, but it is *not* a sentence.

Here's a sentence: The rain flooded the swamp.
Here's an adverb clause: *Until* the rain flooded the swamp, ...

The preposition *until* demands an attached sentence to complete the thought.

Example: Until the rain flooded the swamp, *you could hunt raccoons without fear of drowning.*

Underline the preposition in each adverb phrase or clause below, then write a completion for each sentence.

Example: <u>During</u> the storm, *Sounder slept like a log.*

1. Between the swamp and the field, _____

2. From dawn till dark _____

3. Since David's dad was in jail, _____

4. Until Nathan got home, _____

5. Without an education _____

6. After the trial _____

7. Before the meat was stolen, _____

8. Beneath his calm expression, _____

9. Within the walls of the jail _____

10. Throughout the long journey _____

11. Through all the rough times _____

12. By harvesting her crop without Nathan _____

13. Behind the sheriff's back _____

14. Except for Mrs. Boatwright _____

15. During David's stay at Camille Johnson's school _____

16. Down deep in her soul _____

2. Sounder

Answers

True or False

1. 0   Nathan stole meat because he and his family were hungry.
2. +
3. +
4. 0   Mrs. Johnson invited David to stay at her place and go to school because he is bright.
5. +
6. 0   The sheriff wouldn't tell Mrs. Morgan where her husband was because she was black and he was racist.
7. 0   Mrs. Boatwright's brave act got David the information he needed from the sheriff.
8. 0   Nathan came home early because he was hurt in an accident and couldn't work.
9. 0   Nathan delivers his son to Mrs. Johnson's school so he'll have a chance to live a better life.
10. 0   The movie ends triumphantly as David and Nathan drive off toward Mrs. Johnson's school.

Prepositions

(1) between   (2) of   (3) in   (4) from   (5) to   (6) on   (7) with   (8) to   (9) for   (10) by

(11) by   (12) to   (13) between   (14) like   (15) at   (16) of   (17) about   (18) by   (19) at

(20) for   (21) throughout   (22) in   (23) through   (24) of   (25) in

Prepositional Phrases

Sample answers:

1. Camille Johnson believed that David had learned much *from books.*
2. David believed *in his father.*
3. David put many miles *behind him* as he walked toward Wishbone Labor Camp.
4. David helped his mother *with the chores.*
5. David found little warmth and comfort *along the road* to Nolantown.
6. *For his mother,* David would have walked a hundred miles in search of Nathan.
7. The children were worried *about Sounder.*
8. *At school* David discovered a friend in Camille Johnson.
9. David knew *within his heart* that school was the way to find a new, full life.
10. David spent many days walking *to the prison camp.*

Adverb Phrases and Clauses

Answers for sentence completions will vary. Prepositions to be underlined are as follows:

1. Between	5. Without	9. Within	13. Behind
2. From	6. After	10. Throughout	14. Except
3. Since	7. Before	11. Through	15. During
4. Until	8. Beneath	12. By	16. . . . in

3. SHANE

Author: Jack Schaefer
Novel Title: *Shane*
Director: George Stevens

Running Time: 117 minutes
Year: 1953
Format: color

Summary

On a summer morning in a year just after the Civil War, a stranger rides onto the homestead of a man named Joe Starrett, who is trying to establish a place for himself, his wife Marion, and their son, Joey. The small farm lies in a lush valley at the foot of the Rocky Mountains in western Wyoming. Another man (named Ryker) has laid claim to all the land along the entire valley for his cattle ranch.

The stranger calls himself Shane, is assumed to be one of Ryker's men, and is told to leave, but as he is leaving, Ryker's men show up to challenge Starrett and to try to push him off his land. Shane stays and stands behind Starrett. Joe and Shane become fast friends.

Shane stays on at the Starrett ranch, sensing serious trouble for the Starretts and for all the homesteaders in the valley. Shane's first encounter with Ryker's men is in town at Grafton's store and saloon, where he goes to buy work clothes and a soda pop for Joey. Chris, one of Ryker's roughnecks, threatens Shane, but Shane does not respond. From then on everyone, including the homesteaders, believe Shane is somewhat of a coward.

The homesteaders meet at Joe's house and decide to stick together and face Ryker as a group. So they venture into town to buy supplies and Shane once again enters the bar to return the empty pop bottle. A vicious fight ensues in which Shane is overpowered and beaten by Ryker's men. Joe then joins the fray and together Shane and Joe stand off Ryker's men.

After the fight, Ryker makes a major decision—he will hire a gunslinger from Cheyenne to "deal with" the homesteaders. A few days later a two-gunned stranger named Wilson shows up in town. It isn't long before one of the homesteaders, a hot-tempered fellow named Tory, encounters Wilson and is gunned down in the street. At Tory's funeral Joe decides to do something about Ryker, even if it means killing him.

Marion begs Shane to talk her husband out of his fight with Ryker, but Shane refuses until Chris, the man Shane fought in the bar, sneaks to the Starrett ranch and tells Shane that Joe Starrett will be killed in the saloon if he goes to see Ryker. Shane then literally knocks Joe out in order to keep him from going in to meet Ryker alone.

Shane then straps on his gun and goes to town and kills Ryker, Wilson, and Ryker's brother. Joey follows Shane into town and saves his life by warning him of an ambusher on the stairway landing in the bar. Shane tells Joey good-bye and leaves. He says that a man must be what he is, and knowing that his way of life is outmoded and dangerous, he leaves the safety of the valley and the Starrett ranch for an unsure future farther west. Joey begs Shane to come back, but the stranger leaves the way he came, alone.

Name _____ Date _____

3. Shane

Plot Sequence

The plot of a story, play, or movie is "what happens"—the events that occur one after another. A skilled writer or director makes the events interlock in such a way that the first event seems to cause the second, and the second event seems to cause the third, and so on.

Plot events from the movie *Shane* are listed below, but they are not in order (sequence). Number them as follows: the first event in the movie gets a 1 by it, the second event in the movie gets a 2 on the corresponding line, the third event is numbered 3, and so on.

a. _____ Shane and Joe fight Ryker's men in the saloon.

b. _____ Marion tries to talk Joe out of going into town to face Ryker alone.

c. _____ Joey is sneaking up on a deer when Shane rides up to the ranch.

d. _____ Tory is buried on a hill outside of town.

e. _____ Joe and the other homesteaders hold a meeting at Joe's house and Shane walks out.

f. _____ Joe and Shane chop out the huge stump in Joe's yard.

g. _____ The homesteaders celebrate the Fourth of July at Tory's place.

h. _____ Ryker offers Joe a job.

i. _____ Wilson arrives in town.

j. _____ Tory is gunned down in the street.

k. _____ Shane teaches Joey how to shoot.

l. _____ Mr. Lewis's house is burned by Ryker's men.

m. _____ The homesteaders unite and decide to stay in the valley.

n. _____ Shane kills Wilson.

o. _____ Shane says to Joey, "A man has to be what he is."

p. _____ Shane goes into Grafton's store to buy work clothes.

q. _____ Chris, Ryker's hired man, comes to the Starrett farm and tells Shane that Joe is up against a "stacked deck."

r. _____ Ryker offers Shane a job.

s. _____ Ryker sends off to Cheyenne for a hired gunslinger.

3. Shane

Spelling

Below are ten words spelled with an "able" ending. Using this list, write the word on the line to best complete each sentence below.

respectable   indisputable
punishable   miserable
reliable   charitable
irritable   imaginable
capable   allowable

1. Joe Starrett was a _____, law-abiding man.

2. The conflict with Ryker made most of the homesteaders _____ or cross.

3. The vandalism caused by Ryker's men was _____ by a court of law.

4. Ryker thought that his claim to the land was _____ by anyone.

5. Ryker's plan was to make life so _____ for the home-steaders that they would pack up and leave.

6. Ryker's men did not believe that Shane was _____ of doing them any damage.

7. Joe Starrett was a _____ man who freely helped his neighbors.

8. Joey thought Shane could do anything _____.

9. Joe Starrett and the other homesteaders thought that Ryker should only be able to own the land that was _____ under the law.

10. The other homesteaders looked up to Joe because he was _____ ; he could be depended on to help them when trouble started.

3. Shane

Essay Topics

An essay is not a report. An essay is a written opinion supported by facts, figures, and examples. Below are several topics that could be developed into interesting essays. Choose one and form an opinion about it, then support your opinion with facts and examples from your own life and from the lives of your friends and family. Be sure to write an interesting introduction that "hooks" the reader, and conclude your essay with a strong statement that summarizes exactly how you feel about the issue.

1. Individual Freedom
At one point, Joe Starrett says that Ryker can't go around telling the people what their rights are. Ryker disagrees with Joe. Ryker feels he was there first and should have the say about who does what in the valley.
- Do you agree with Joe? Or does Ryker have a point? What are Joe's rights as a homesteader?
- Does having freedom mean anyone can do anything he or she wants?
- What does individual freedom mean? What *is* freedom, anyway?
- Is there ever a time when you would actually fight for your rights? Why or why not?

2. Gun Control
Marion, Joe's wife, believes that the whole valley would be much better off if guns didn't exist. Do you agree with her? Why or why not?

3. Change
At the end of the film Shane says that no one can really change what he or she is.
- Do you agree or disagree?
- Is change a good thing or a bad thing?
- Have you changed? How? When? What were the effects?

4. Heroes
Shane is a hero to Joey for a lot of reasons.
- Do you think Shane is a hero? What is a hero, anyway?
- Do we have any "real" heroes today? Are you a hero? In what ways? If you're not a hero today, what would you have to do to become one?

5. Friends
Shane and Joe become good friends. They care about each other and understand one another. In your opinion, what makes a good friend?

3. Shane

Projects

Sometimes by watching a movie you get inspired to *do* something. Below are some ideas that might inspire you to use your imagination and craft skills to make or demonstrate something based on the events in the movie *Shane*. Most projects shouldn't take more than a couple of days, and they use materials that are fairly easy to get.

Choose one of the projects listed or create one of your own. When it is completed, set up a display table in the hall or out in front of the office at your school, or take several of the class projects to the senior citizens' center in your community and set them out for viewing. Or you might display your work in a medical center, hospital, rest home, or local shopping mall. Or a group of you might get together and build one project and enter it in the county fair during the summer.

1. Build a papier-mâché model of the valley where the Starretts live. Paint in the river, build a mountain range, a cabin, a corral, barn, and wagon shed to resemble the Starrett homestead. You'll have to imagine the clouds, unless you can find a way to dangle cotton balls over your masterpiece.

2. When the Starretts and other homesteaders went into town it was a trip they couldn't waste, so they took a wagon in which to haul supplies. Build a model of one of these sturdy vehicles out of pine wood, clay, or cardboard, and be careful to put in all the details. An original "buckboard" contained hundreds of parts: springs, bolts, straps, spoked wheels, and so forth. You may want to go to an encyclopedia or to a book about pioneer life in order to get the best information, unless, of course, you have an antiques dealer or wagon builder living in your community.

3. Using colored artist's charcoal or pastel crayons, sketch a scene involving Shane on his horse. You could use any scene that struck your fancy. But be careful. Many artists say that the horse is the hardest thing to "capture" on paper.

4. Make a poster advertising free land out West. Millions of these were made when people first homesteaded land in Canada, the United States, and Australia. People in cities or towns who were restless or land-poor would hear about the wonderful acres available to them for "nothing"! But the posters and leaflets didn't tell the whole story. They were made to entice people to leave their homes and farms and come to the "new land" where hard work alone could earn them a vast number of acres. Get out your pencil and paints and see what kind of advertising poster you can create.

3. Shane

Answers

Plot Sequence

(a)	6	(f)	2	(k)	9	(p)	3
(b)	16	(g)	10	(l)	14	(q)	17
(c)	1	(h)	11	(m)	15	(r)	5
(d)	13	(i)	8	(n)	18	(s)	7
(e)	4	(j)	12	(o)	19		

Spelling

(1) respectable   (6) capable

(2) irritable   (7) charitable

(3) punishable   (8) imaginable

(4) indisputable   (9) allowable

(5) miserable   (10) reliable

Essay Topics

Essays will vary.

Projects

Projects will vary.

4. WHERE THE RED FERN GROWS

Author: Wilson Rawls
Novel Title: *Where the Red Fern Grows*
Director: Norman Tokar

Running Time: 100 minutes
Year: 1974
Format: color

Summary

Where the Red Fern Grows is about a boy who learns the meaning of love through his relationship with two hunting hounds in the Ozark mountains.

Billy Coleman, a young farm boy, eats, sleeps, and even dreams about hound puppies. He wants a pair of fine hounds for treeing raccoons, and despairs because they cost money and it is during the Depression of the 1920's and '30's. He tells his grandfather that he's been praying for dogs for years, but Grandpa replies, "You've got to do your share—meet God halfway."

Billy goes to work for the neighbors in his spare time and saves forty dollars. Then he brings his stash to Grandpa, owner of the local general store, who orders the dogs for Billy out of a catalog. The dogs arrive, but they're in Tallequah, several miles downriver. Billy skips out of the house at night and walks all the way to get his dogs. He fights the town boys and meets the kindly sheriff, who stops the fight and sends him on his way.

Billy fights off a mountain lion who prowls near the cave in which Billy and the pups camp for the night. The next day, while drinking from a river, Billy finds the names Dan and Ann carved in a sycamore tree. He gives these names to his pups, and he goes home bearing gifts: overalls for his dad, calico cloth for his mother, and candy for his sisters.

Billy trains the dogs till they are expert hunters, then accepts the challenge of the neighboring bullies, the Pritchart boys, to tree the "ghost coon." Dan and Ann tree the raccoon, then the Pritcharts' hound, Old Blue, shows up and he and Dan get into a fight. Rubin Pritchart won't pay the two-dollar bet, so Billy and he struggle over the money. Rubin reaches for Billy's belt axe to kill Dan and Ann, who he believes are killing Old Blue. Billy trips Rubin, and Rubin falls on the axe and dies. At the funeral, Billy swears off raccoon hunting forever.

A few weeks pass and Grandpa announces one day at supper that he's signed up Dan and Ann for the District 7 National Raccoon Hunting Competition. Billy hedges, but then realizes that his hounds should have the right to prove themselves the best in the country.

On the final night of competition Grandpa is hurt, and Billy calls off his dogs to find his grandfather, thus officially losing the gold cup and the cash pool. The awards go to Sam Bellington, who has won three times previously. No one claps during the ceremony—until Billy gives Sam a round of applause, breaking the ice. Sam awards Billy the gold cup and the money, and Billy is declared the champion.

Billy continues to hunt till one night when his dogs tree a mountain lion that attacks him. Old Dan leaps on the mountain lion, and while it's occupied, Billy kills it with his axe. But Old Dan is fatally slashed by the lion's claws. He dies shortly thereafter, then Little Ann dies of grief.

Billy cannot understand why both his dogs "had to die," but now the family can move to Tulsa and take over their uncle's hardware business and provide better opportunities for Billy and his sisters. Just before leaving, Billy visits the graves of Old Dan and Little Ann and sees a red fern—the symbol of undying love—growing between the graves. It is a sign that everything is all right and was meant to be. The family leaves for Tulsa.

The narrator states that he has never returned to the Ozarks, but would like to see once again the hills he roamed as a boy, the sycamore tree with Dan and Ann carved in it, and the place by the river where the red fern grows.

4. Where the Red Fern Grows

Pronouns

Pronouns are words that replace nouns. Without pronouns many sentences would sound ridiculous: "Jim fell and broke Jim's nose" makes no sense at all. But: "Jim fell and broke his nose" is perfectly clear.

The trick is to use the correct pronoun in its proper place. When you use a pronoun as the subject of a sentence you must use one of the following five choices: I, he, she, we, they. You cannot say: "Them are my shoes" because *them* is not a subject pronoun. You have to say: "They are my shoes" or simply, "They're mine!"

Below are several sentences that include one or more pronouns. Circle the correct pronoun in each sentence, and remember—the five choices listed above are only correct when they are used as subjects of sentences or clauses.

1. (Us, We) were invited to supper at Grandpa's house.

2. (He, Him) was a boy with a lot of grit.

3. (I, Me) have never seen a better example of courage.

4. (They, Them) were the best pair of hounds in the Ozarks.

5. (She, Her) was a good friend to the big dog, Dan.

6. Dan and (her, she) would run all night after raccoons.

7. (Me, I) and my friend had never seen such fine hounds.

8. (They, Them) and (we, us) are the only people with any chance of winning this hunting competition.

9. (Us, We) were ready for anything the raccoons could try on (we, us).

10. Nobody believed (us, we) when (us, we) told them about Billy's dogs.

11. The dogs ran in front of (they, them) and (us, we) all night.

12. "(Them, They) are fine hounds," said the sheriff.

13. After Rubin died, Billy said (him, he) would never hunt again.

14. (He, Him) couldn't keep his dogs from doing what (them, they) were born to do.

15. (I, Me) have never seen a more dedicated hunter or better sportsman.

Name _____   Date _____

4. Where the Red Fern Grows

Verbs—Past Participle

Verbs not only show action; they also tell time. You can say:

I am eating. (present)
I just ate. (past)
I have eaten. (past participle)

The past participle form is most bothersome because it sounds strange to the ear: "I have just *swum* across the English Channel" sounds weird because few people say *swum* in everyday talk. Some other past participles are: *fallen, ridden, frozen, chosen, stolen, drunk, written, hidden, rung, sung, hung, brought, burst, given, gone, done, known, begun, driven, blown,* and *lain.*

Circle the past participle in each of the sentences below.

1. After Dan and Ann had (drove, driven) the raccoon up the sycamore tree, Billy realized what a gigantic task it was going to be to chop it down.

2. Billy must have (swang, swung) the axe a thousand times before the wind came up.

3. If the wind hadn't (blew, blown) the tree over, it might have (stood, standed) there a long time.

4. Billy's father felt that his son had (became, become) a man.

5. Billy's mother believed that her boy had (gone, went) "coon crazy."

6. Grandpa was sorry he had ever (gave, given) Billy the two dollars for the "Ghost Raccoon" bet.

7. Billy believed his dogs would catch the "Ghost Raccoon" long before the hunt had (begun, began).

8. If only Billy had (knew, known) that Rubin would never live to see another day, he would never have gone after the "Ghost Raccoon."

9. Rubin was (knowing, known) for his dishonest and rowdy behavior.

10. If he'd been decent and had (gave, given) Billy his two dollars when the "Ghost Raccoon" was (finded, found), Rubin would not have died the way he did.

4. Where the Red Fern Grows

Journal Entry

Keeping journals is an old practice. Pioneers who settled America often wrote daily accounts of their journey, the struggles, pain, and good fortune of their days. In fact, many people keep journals today. They want to "think on paper" with only themselves as an audience, or they may want to leave a written legacy for their children and grandchildren.

Pretend you are Billy Coleman at the state championship hunting dog competition. Write a journal entry that tells what's going through your mind on the night before your dogs compete. What would you be afraid of? What would you want to have happen?

The Journal of Billy C. — The Championship

_____

_____

_____

_____

_____

_____

_____

_____

_____

_____

_____

_____

4. Where the Red Fern Grows

Essay Topics

Choose one of the topics below and write an interesting essay describing the topic, arguing the opinion, or telling the story.

1. The City or the Country?

Many people believe that city life provides the best opportunities for people. A city has museums, universities, libraries, opera halls, civic centers, and advanced medical services. All these things contribute to a high quality of life. Other people think that country life, away from all the pollution, crime, noise, and crowds, gives a person the best chance to experience nature and to find his or her own best way to live a good life. What do you think?

2. Papa Needs a New Mule

When Billy earns the money for his dogs, he does it in secret; he doesn't tell his father. The needs of the family are important; if his dad knew he had that much money, chances are he'd want it for a new mule to farm with rather than a pair of dogs. When Billy finally goes to order the dogs, he faces a moral dilemma: Should he buy the dogs or not? Describe Billy's feelings and thoughts as he stands at the counter with forty dollars in his hand.

3. A Night in the Woods

Describe Billy's night of fear in the cave by the river. The cougar is out there trying to get his pups. He's a long way from home. He has no weapons. How does he spend the night? What night sounds does he hear? Is he cold? Hungry? Worried? What does he wish he had done to better prepare for the trip? Does he wish he'd never taken the journey?

4. The Best Kind of Love

The red fern is the symbol of the "best kind of love." In your opinion, what is the best kind of love a person can give or receive? Is that kind of love possible in today's modern society? Are you capable of giving that kind of love? How can you express the "best kind of love" in your daily life?

5. Rubin and Billy: Two Boys from the Hills

Contrast the lives of Rubin Pritchart and Billy Coleman. What kind of home did each one come from? How did each boy "see" life—positively or negatively? How honest, hardworking, caring, and sportsmanlike was each boy? What was the main difference between them?

4. Where the Red Fern Grows

Answers

Pronouns

(1) we   (6) she   (11) them; us

(2) he   (7) I   (12) they

(3) I   (8) they; we   (13) he

(4) they   (9) we; us   (14) he; they

(5) she   (10) us; we   (15) I

Verbs—Past Participle

(1) driven   (6) given

(2) swung   (7) begun

(3) blown; stood   (8) known

(4) become   (9) known

(5) gone   (10) given; found

Journal Entry

Sample:

I'm sitting here alone in the tent while Dad and Grandpa are talking to some of the men two tents down from ours. They are having as much fun as I am. There are so many hunters here. I know Dan and Ann are good, but are they the best? I'm the only one who thinks so (Grandpa and Dad too). The others think their dogs are best, but Dan and Ann will show them "what for" tomorrow.

If they don't, I'm afraid of what Grandpa will think. He's wanted this longer than I have. I never realized what this meant to him till I saw the look on his face when we pulled in here and signed up Dan and Ann with the sheriff, who is running this contest. Grandpa sure was proud. I hope he's still that way after tomorrow night.

Essay Topics

Essays will vary.

5. THE MIRACLE WORKER

Author: William Gibson
Play Title: *The Miracle Worker*
Director: Arthur Penn

Running Time: 107 minutes
Year: 1962
Format: black and white

Summary

Annie Sullivan, a 19-year-old student at the Perkins School for the Blind, in Boston, Massachusetts, is hired by a wealthy southern family named Keller to help their blind and deaf child, Helen, learn to communicate.

When Annie arrives, she finds Helen acting and being treated like an animal. Helen rips and smashes anything she finds handy when she's angry (which is often), she grabs fistfuls of food off anyone's plate at dinnertime, stuffing it in her mouth like a chimpanzee, and she grunts like a beast now and then because she can't form words or anything that comes close to language.

Annie is appalled at the way the girl is treated and begins to take things in hand the moment she arrives. She brings a doll for Helen, which the girl uses to smash Annie in the face, knocking out one of her teeth. This does not discourage the young teacher. She knows Helen is bright and frustrated with her limited world. Annie decides to rescue her from the prison in which the child has been locked for years.

Helen locks Annie in her room on their first meeting, and Miss Sullivan must climb out the upstairs bedroom window and get down with the help of a ladder and Helen's father, Captain Keller, an ex-Civil War officer.

In the next major scene, Annie teaches Helen some basic table manners: eating with utensils, folding a napkin, sitting in a chair and staying there throughout a meal. It's a violent, exhausting struggle. Annie wins the pitched battle, but Mr. and Mrs. Keller refuse to support her efforts with Helen. They continue to indulge the child and mistrust Annie. Finally, Annie requests to have the empty cottage on the property furnished for her and Helen, and asks that she be the only one to see Helen for two weeks, night or day.

At the cottage, Helen learns to rely on Annie; they get closer as student and teacher. But still, Helen does not learn that the "word game" (Annie spells words into Helen's hand) has any connection with the objects in the world around her. Helen can spell by imitating, but does not "see" the words as symbols. Captain Keller finally steps in and demands that his daughter be returned to the house and the "normal" life they have all been living. Annie resists, but must consent.

At their final meal together, Helen tests Annie and the family by reverting to her "animal" ways around the table. The Kellers are willing to let it happen all over again. A moment comes when Helen runs for her mother's lap, and Annie issues an ultimatum: Mrs. Keller either releases Helen to Annie's care, or keeps her and lets her remain in darkness. Mrs. Keller releases Helen, literally, and the girl immediately throws a pitcher of water in Annie's face. Annie leaps to her feet, grabs Helen, and drags her outside to the pump to fill up the pitcher. Captain Keller is furious, but is stopped in his tirade by his son, Jimmy, who bars the door and tells the Captain he's "consummately wrong."

Annie and Helen are outside filling up the water pitcher when Annie, in a last, desperate move, spells W-A-T-E-R into Helen's hand—and Helen understands. She spells it back—splashes water on her face, then spells W-A-T-E-R again. She has learned. Helen can "see" and her world is opened.

In a final gesture, Helen hands to Annie the keys she has used to lock other teachers and "tormentors" out of her life. Then she spells "teacher" into Annie's hand. They have unlocked something in each other.

5. The Miracle Worker

Quiz

Below are 16 questions to check your comprehension of events in the movie *The Miracle Worker.* There are 10 true/false questions, and 6 multiple choice. Write your answers on the line after each number.

True or False: Mark the true statements below with a plus sign (+), and mark the false statements with a zero (0).

1. ____ Annie Sullivan was sent to the Kellers because she had taught so successfully at the Perkins School in Boston.

2. ____ Annie Sullivan said, "It's easier to teach her (Helen) something than to feel sorry for her!"

3. ____ Before Annie Sullivan came, Helen had spoken only one syllable in her life.

4. ____ Annie is often tormented by thoughts and dreams of her past.

5. ____ Helen was made blind and deaf by a bad fall from a fence.

6. ____ When Helen spilled ink all over Annie's papers, Annie punished Helen to teach her self-control.

7. ____ Captain Keller supported Annie Sullivan's methods completely.

8. ____ In the film, Jimmy Keller never really resisted Captain Keller, except for once.

9. ____ Annie Sullivan taught the Keller family that discipline is an important part of real love.

10. ____ Helen gave the key to her room, and to her heart, to Jimmy at the end of the movie.

(*Quiz continued on next page*)

Name _____ Date _____

5. The Miracle Worker

Quiz (continued)

Multiple Choice: Determine the correct answer for each question below, then write the letter on the line after the number. Be careful—read all six possible choices before answering.

11. ____ Annie taught Helen using: (a) Braille (b) body language (c) sound signals (d) letters spelled into Helen's palm (e) none of the above (f) both "c" and "d"

12. ____ Helen was helped to learn by all of these factors *except*:
    (a) Captain Keller could afford to hire a private teacher for Helen.
    (b) Annie Sullivan was a strong-willed, intelligent person.
    (c) Helen had a memory of saying "Wa," which meant water, as a six-month-old child.
    (d) Jimmy Keller finally stood up to Captain Keller.
    (e) Annie kept her past life a secret from all except Jimmy.
    (f) All of the above.

13. ____ Annie said her life in the asylum: (a) made her bitter (b) taught her about death (c) made her rich (d) made her strong (e) all of the above (f) both "a" and "d"

14. ____ Annie Sullivan's blindness and hard childhood made it possible to: (a) understand what Helen was going through, and to stick with the task of helping Helen (b) hate Captain Keller (c) spoil Helen even more (d) hate Jimmy Keller (e) all of the above (f) none of the above

15. ____ Helen's family allowed her to eat like an animal because: (a) a former teacher told them it was the right thing to do (b) Jimmy thought it was funny (c) Captain Keller was afraid of Helen (d) they thought that letting her be "free" was the best way to love her (e) all of the above (f) both "a" and "d"

16. ____ Captain Keller thought Annie Sullivan was rude because she: (a) spanked Helen (b) spoke her mind to him (c) ate with no napkin (d) was a poor teacher (e) none of the above (f) both "c" and "d"

5. The Miracle Worker

Symbolism

A cattle brand is a symbol—it represents the ranch to which an animal belongs. Letters of the alphabet are symbols that stand for sounds. Objects can be symbols as well. The flag of Canada represents the nation of Canada. The official seal of the government of Australia represents the nation of Australia on all documents upon which the seal is used.

There are also symbols in literature and film—the white napkin that Helen throws to the floor during the final dinner scene in *The Miracle Worker* is a symbol that represents Helen's rebellion against what Annie Sullivan is trying to do. The twist here is that a white flag or cloth usually means surrender, but the director of the film used the opposite meaning in this instance.

Decide what character or idea each object below symbolized in *The Miracle Worker*, and then tell how the symbol is important to the message of the film.

Doll _____

_____

_____

_____

Dog _____

_____

_____

_____

Key _____

_____

_____

_____

Well _____

_____

_____

_____

5. The Miracle Worker

Spelling

When you add the "-able" ending to words in English, you often get adjectives, words that describe nouns. Below are ten "-able" words, most of them adjectives. Choose the word that best fits in each sentence below, and write it on the line provided.

dependable   unbearable   likable
irritable   capable   excusable
desirable   available   syllable
                  liable

1. Many teachers might think that working with Helen Keller would not be a very _____ job; but not Annie Sullivan. She saw it as a challenge.

2. Helen was not really a very _____ person most of the time.

3. Working with Helen's parents was sometimes more _____ than working with Helen.

4. Helen's parents thought that her behavior was _____, since she was blind and could not hear, and had to do without the many benefits of a normal life.

5. Annie knew that Helen was _____ of much more than her family was expecting of her.

6. Helen was _____ to become _____ at any given moment.

7. Helen's mother told Annie that Helen had uttered only one _____ in her life: "Wa."

8. Annie Sullivan used every means _____ to help Helen out of her dark, silent tomb of ignorance.

9. It was lucky for Helen that Annie was a _____, responsible person who was not about to run off and leave her.

5. The Miracle Worker

Answers

Quiz

(1) +	(6) 0	(11) d	(16) b
(2) 0	(7) 0	(12) e	
(3) +	(8) +	(13) d	
(4) +	(9) +	(14) a	
(5) +	(10) 0	(15) f	

Symbolism

Doll—The doll represents the plaything that Helen has become in the hands of her family. Like Helen, the doll cannot speak, hear, or talk. On the surface it is a gift from Annie to Helen, but its other significance as a symbol of what Helen has become is critical to the story.

Dog—The family pet, who gobbles food off a plate and begs for more, is symbolic of Helen again in her role in the family. The symbol seems to say that if Annie doesn't improve this child's life by teaching her to communicate with the world, Helen will be an "animal" all her life.

Key—The "key" to Helen's deliverance from darkness is Annie Sullivan. The symbol also can be taken to mean "education" or "learning" as a key to Helen's future. When Helen hands Annie the key at the end of the film, Helen is saying, "Free me. Open up the door. I give you permission to change me into a real, thinking human being."

Well— A well provides one of the main elements of existence—water. When Helen spells W-A-T-E-R, it is her liberating moment. The physical symbol of life has now taken on an additional significance—learning, communicating, "seeing." Now that Helen has the communication tools, she has uncovered a "well" of knowledge that she can partake of for the rest of her life.

Spelling

(1) desirable

(2) likable

(3) unbearable

(4) excusable

(5) capable

(6) liable; irritable

(7) syllable

(8) available

(9) dependable

6. ANNE OF GREEN GABLES

Author: L. M. Montgomery
Novel Title: *Anne of Green Gables*
Director: Kevin Sullivan

Running Time: 197 minutes
Year: 1987
Format: color

Summary

After being sent back to the orphanage for being lofty-headed, Anne Shirley is given the news that she's being taken in by a family on Prince Edward Island. Anne is overjoyed until at the Cuthbert home she finds that there has been a "tragical" mistake—they had wanted a boy, not a girl, and Anne will have to be sent back. Matthew Cuthbert, the elderly co-owner of Green Gables, wants to keep the girl, but his sister, Marilla, will have nothing of it, and carts the girl back to the orphanage the next day. But there Anne's fortunes change as a nasty Mrs. Blewett just happens to show up looking for a girl to do her housework and to care for her large brood of children. Marilla will not turn Anne over to such a woman, and returns to Green Gables "to get Matthew's opinion," which she already has.

Anne encounters difficulties right from the start: she doesn't have enough "religion" to please Marilla, she is accused of stealing Marilla's prized brooch, which later turns up, and Anne insults Marilla's neighbor, Rachel Lynde, when Rachel belittles Anne's appearance, especially Anne's red hair. But Anne apologizes after being encouraged by Matthew, and sets her sights on the church picnic.

At the picnic she meets a "bosom friend," Dianna Berry, and together they defeat all the boys in a race, including Gilbert Blithe, whose father was Marilla's spurned sweetheart years ago. At school, Anne breaks a slate over Gilbert's head because he called her "Carrots." Then she dyes her hair green and is chided by Marilla for being vain. That spring she excels in school, earning grades second only to Gilbert Blithe's. Her future is beginning to take shape around her academic prowess. Gilbert Blithe is impressed and begins to fall in love with Anne.

Anne holds an afternoon tea for her dear friend, Dianna Berry, but things go awry. Dianna gets drunk on brandy that Anne thought was raspberry cordial, a fruit drink, and Dianna's mother forbids Anne to ever see Dianna again. But one night while all the adults but Matthew are gone from the area for a political rally, Dianna runs to Anne for help. Her baby sister's got the croup, a suffocating sickness, and Anne applies massive doses of ipecac, an expectorant, and saves the baby's life. Anne is a heroine from here on. She ingratiates herself to Dianna's rich aunt, who invites the girl to come to her mansion to visit. While there, Anne takes the entrance exam for Queens College and wins a scholarship.

At Queens College she earns a teaching degree through an accelerated program, along with a four-year, full-tuition Avery Scholarship to a very respectable institution.

At home one day, Anne is walking toward the house and sees Matthew fall headlong into the grass. His heart has given out. He dies in her arms. Following Matthew's death, a Mr. Saddler offers to buy Green Gables, and Marilla can see no other way to go. Anne gives up her scholarship and applies for a teaching job close to home so she can stay with Marilla and help out financially. Gilbert hears of her plans and gives up his job at the local school so Anne can work near home and live at Green Gables.

Marilla encourages Anne to make up with Gilbert, because Anne has been at odds with him ever since she beat him in the three-legged race years ago. The film ends as she walks off with Gilbert, having realized that there are more "kindred spirits" out there than she ever suspected.

6. Anne of Green Gables

Questions

1. Write some brief thoughts that might have been going through Anne's mind as she left Green Gables the day she was to be brought back to the children's asylum.

   _____

   _____

2. Why didn't Marilla leave Anne with Mrs. Blewett?

   _____

3. What did Mrs. Blewett say that disturbed Marilla?

   _____

4. How does Matthew's love for Anne keep her from being sent away from Green Gables?

   _____

5. How does Anne temporarily "lose" her best friend, Dianna Berry?

   _____

6. How does Anne "win" Dianna back?

   _____

7. Anne is invited to dinner at Dianna's house and Marilla says that "humble pie" is probably on the menu. What does she mean? Explain.

   _____

8. When Anne competes for a scholarship to college she worries over the results. She says, "I'd rather not place, than be in the middle." Why does she feel this way? Explain.

   _____

   _____

9. Why does Anne decide not to go back to college, but to teach near home?

   _____

10. What does Gilbert do to help Anne stay near home?

   _____

6. Anne of Green Gables

Inferences

In the movie *Anne of Green Gables*, many phrases are used and sentences spoken that take some thought to completely understand. Read the words below spoken by various characters in the movie. On the lines provided, explain in your own words what the sentences mean. What are the main ideas behind these statements?

1. When Matthew arrives to pick up his "boy," the railroad ticket agent says, "She's got a tongue of her own!" Explain what he meant by this statement about Anne Shirley.

   _____

   _____

2. Matthew and Marilla are talking about Anne. Marilla says, "Matthew, don't put your oar in." Explain:

   _____

   _____

3. Matthew says to Marilla: "Maybe we might be of some good to her." Explain: _____

   _____

4. Marilla says to Anne, "God does not want you for a fair-weather friend." Explain: _____

   _____

5. Marilla tells Anne: "To despair is to turn your back on God." Explain:

   _____

   _____

6. Miss Stacy, Anne's teacher and friend, say to Anne: "The Truth shall set you free."
   Explain: _____

   _____

7. Anne says: "Tomorrow is always fresh. There are no mistakes in it." What does she mean?

   _____

   _____

6. Anne of Green Gables

Writing—Kindred Spirits

In the film *Anne of Green Gables*, Anne Shirley begins as a dreamy-headed orphan whom no one wants. She is lonely and makes up imaginary friends and reads romantic poems and books, dreaming of the day when a knight in shining armor will rescue her from despair.

Once Anne is adopted by the Cuthberts she begins to meet people she calls "kindred spirits." Define a kindred spirit on the lines below, then list three of Anne's kindred spirits as portrayed in the movie. Tell why each is a kindred spirit. Describe Anne's relationship to each of these people.

Finally, on the lines at the bottom of the page, name someone who is a kindred spirit to you. Describe your relationship to him or her and tell how you intend to keep the relationship strong.

1. Define "kindred spirit": _____

_____

2. Anne's Kindred Spirit #1: _____

Explain: _____

_____

3. Anne's Kindred Spirit #2: _____

Explain: _____

_____

4. Anne's Kindred Spirit #3: _____

Explain: _____

_____

5. Name of *your* kindred spirit: _____

Explain: _____

_____

_____

_____

_____

6. Anne of Green Gables

Travel Brochure

The story of Anne Shirley takes place on Prince Edward Island, Canada. It is a beautiful, windblown island surrounded by ocean and sand, and occupied by magnificent homes and fields that are farmed to perfection. Such places inspire people to visit and make a vacation out of seeing Prince Edward Island and the property where the movie *Anne of Green Gables* was made.

Pretend for a moment that you are the travel director for an exotic location somewhere other than your home country. Look up what information you can on the place—in books and pamphlets from tourist bureaus, travel bureaus, chambers of commerce in capital cities, and from interviewing people who may have visited the place you are researching. Then do the following:

1. Make a folder with a drawing of your exotic location on the cover.

2. Inside the folder, place rough copies (first drafts) of the following pieces of information:

   a. a list of 20 adjectives describing the area

   b. a map of the area showing all the special places to see

   c. sketches of particularly beautiful and interesting spots to visit (If you'd prefer not to include sketches, cut out pictures of your vacation hot-spot from brochures and magazines you've found that feature your location, or that resemble it.)

   d. a letter addressed to "Dear Visitor" telling the best reasons for vacationing in your exotic place

   e. a report with basic information about costs, weather, travel times, phone numbers, train schedules, airline reservations, hotels, tours, recommended clothing, etc.

3. Take a sheet of 8½" x 11" paper and fold it in three sections like a brochure, so that the final dimensions are approximately 8" x 3⅝" when folded shut. Then use a word processor, typewriter, or a fine black marker to copy the most important, impressive information from your sheets of "first draft" copies in your folder. You'll have to redraw your sketches to fit the smaller sized brochure or use the smaller pictures to fit on the folded pages. When you have finished, photocopy your brochure so that each of your classmates gets a copy.

6. Anne of Green Gables

Answers

Questions

1. "I have never had a dream come true. Maybe life is only beautiful in books. If that's so, then I don't want to do anything else but read. I wish I were a boy, then none of this would be happening to me."
2. Marilla didn't approve of Mrs. Blewett's callous regard for Anne; Mrs. Blewett treated the girl like a mule.
3. "I don't know but the skinny ones can work the hardest."
4. Matthew talks Anne into apologizing to Rachel.
5. Dianna accidentally gets drunk at Anne's tea party, and Dianna's mother blames Anne.
6. Anne saves the life of Dianna's little sister.
7. Marilla means that Mrs. Berry is going to be forced to apologize, under the circumstances.
8. She wants to be the best, and will not settle for anything less. She'd rather not compete.
9. Since Matthew has died, Anne wants to keep Marilla company.
10. Gilbert gives up his teaching job in Avon Lea so Anne can have it.

Inferences

1. Anne is capable of saying what she means in her own way, on her own terms, without fear. She is a bright and independent person.
2. Marilla means Matthew should let her raise Anne without any input or advice from him.
3. Matthew means that they shouldn't view Anne as hired help, but as a child in need.
4. Marilla means that God wants people to have strong faith even when things go sour.
5. Marilla means that to be sad about what God has ordained to happen is to insult His ability to know what's best for us.
6. Miss Stacy means that lies force you to cover up with more lies. The truth allows you to be open and carefree because you do not have to watch every word you say.
7. No matter what we've done or what has happened on a particular day, the next day is like a blank slate upon which we may write a whole new plan of action.

Writing

1. A kindred spirit is a person who sees the world as we do, who celebrates the same things, who mourns over the same sorrows.
2. Dianna Berry—she sees the world as a place of adventure and fun, as Anne does. She enjoys traveling, reading, talking, and laughing. Anne loves her as a true friend.
3. Miss Stacy—she loves learning and books and the challenge of discovering new ideas. She is happy with her success as a professional, and strives for excellence as Anne does.
4. Matthew Cuthbert—he was gentle, kind, and loving. He loved the land and appreciated the beauty of nature. He was independent, as Anne was, but not to the point of needing no one else. He enjoyed sharing his life with others, as Anne did.
5. Answers will vary.

Travel Brochure

Examples will vary.

7. THE DIARY OF ANNE FRANK

Author: Anne Frank
Book Title: *Diary of Anne Frank*
Director: George Stevens

Running Time: 170 minutes
Year: 1959
Format: black and white

Summary

Anne Frank, a young Dutch Jewish girl, is hiding in a secret room in her father Otto Frank's spice factory because the Nazis will send the family to a concentration camp if they are found. She is locked away with her sister, Margot; her mother; Mr. and Mrs. Van Daan and their son, Peter; and a stranger named Mr. Dussel, who is brought to the room by Mr. Krayler, Otto Frank's business associate.

The Franks spend over two years in the small rooms whose door to the outside world is a swinging bookcase built into the wall. Their food and supplies are brought by a secretary named Miep, and by Mr. Krayler. It is a dangerous situation, and at times life in the secret room is almost unbearable.

Anne and Peter become attracted to each other and talk about their plans for the future and share how they feel toward each other. Mr. Dussell, whose room is next to Anne's, is a constant source of irritation with his fussy ways and crotchety behavior. The Van Daans fight continually and Mr. Van Daan's petty ways set the group at each other's throats when he steals bread one night from the small supply in the room. Mrs. Frank wants him out, immediately, but Mr. Van Daan breaks down and weeps over his foolish behavior.

It's D-Day and the captives rejoice; their freedom will come soon now. But a burglar who has visited the spice factory once before returns, and when Peter's cat knocks a dish off the shelf the burglar is spooked and runs out. Mr. Dussel says that the thief will be caught someday and will tell them in order to get off.

The group waits in fear, and one day their fears are realized—German soldiers show up to check the factory. Peter's cat meows and the Germans draw closer to the bookcase entrance, but then they meow back to the cat, laugh nervously, and leave.

Life goes back to some sense of normalcy— Anne and Peter tease and talk, Miep and Mr. Krayler bring food parcels and news and a radio concealed in a book. The group celebrates Hanukkah and Anne makes everyone a present, even crabby Mr. Dussel.

Then one day while Anne and Peter are talking about religion and about their futures, a pounding is heard at the door. The Germans have come. They burst in, arrest everyone, and ransack the room, leaving Anne's diary behind. The family is taken to a concentration camp, and Anne's last words to Peter echo ominously in the viewer's mind: "In spite of everything, I still think everyone is good at heart."

Footnote: Anne Frank died at age 15 in a German concentration camp, just a few months before World War II ended in German defeat.

7. The Diary of Anne Frank

Identifying Characters

Match the characters with their personal descriptions by writing the letter of the character on the line next to that character's description. Some letters will be used more than once.

Characters:

a. Anne Frank   b. Otto Frank   c. Edith Frank   d. Margot Frank
e. Mr. Van Daan   f. Peter Van Daan   g. Mrs. Van Daan
h. Mr. Dussel   i. Miep   j. Mr. Krayler

1. _____ kept a diary

2. _____ loved "Mooshi"

3. _____ was highly respected by everyone

4. _____ stole bread from the children

5. _____ smoked cigarettes

6. _____ wore earplugs

7. _____ had an allergy to "furbearing" animals

8. _____ gave Anne a diary

9. _____ was a good and quiet daughter

10. _____ told the Van Daans to get out

11. _____ had nice legs

12. _____ wanted to live even after her death

13. _____ talks to Anne behind closed doors

14. _____ says, "They will catch the thief, and he will turn us in."

15. _____ makes her mother cry

16. _____ says, "I love no one but you, Father."

17. _____ brings a chocolate cake to the hideout

18. _____ insists that Mrs. Frank cut the cake

19. _____ says, "To think of the day when a man like Mr. Frank would have
to go into hiding."

20. _____ says, "We lived in fear; now we can live in hope."

7. The Diary of Anne Frank

Newspaper Article

Few people knew of the ordeal that the Franks, the Van Daans, Mr. Dussel, Miep, and Mr. Krayler endured during those twenty-five months in the attic while the Nazis occupied Holland. Only later did the story come out.

Imagine yourself as the only reporter ever to have interviewed the group. You are a friend of Miep and you met with the group in secret two days before the Nazis came to take them away. Now the war is over and you decide to print the story of these brave, doomed people.

In the columns below, tell what you saw, what they said, how they acted, and how you reacted to the stress and fear and hope that they lived with in those final hours. Remember: News stories tell Who, What, When, Where, and Why or How. You can use quotes from any of the characters you "interviewed" to help tell the story.

The Holland Herald

Local Citizens Spend Two Years in Hiding

by _____ (*your name*)

7. The Diary of Anne Frank

Self-Analysis

The great American writer Mark Twain once said, "Everyone is a moon, with a dark side that he doesn't show to anyone." While this may be true, we find Anne Frank being very honest in her diary about what she was like, both the "good" side and the "bad" side.

Below, in the two halves of the "moon," list some things about yourself that you consider good and "bad"—attitudes that are helpful to you and to others, and some that may not be helpful in getting along with people. Then pair off with a classmate whom you trust and compare one or two things from each half of your "moon" (your personality). Do you have any suggestions for your classmate on how to improve a couple of the items in the gray area? Does your classmate have any helpful suggestions for you, things that worked for him or her in the past?

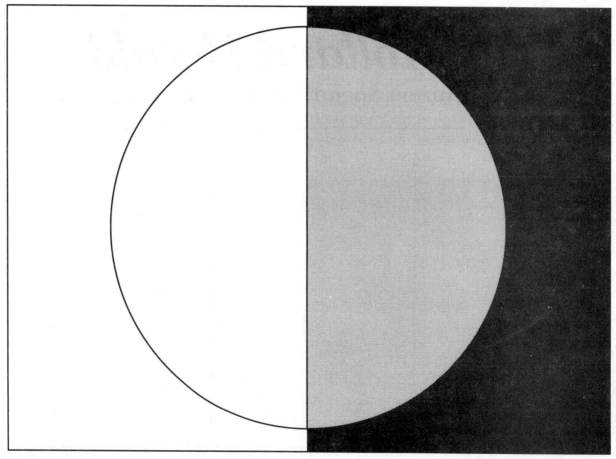

7. The Diary of Anne Frank

Creative Writing

Anne Frank says that her family was to "disappear, to vanish" as if they'd been swept away like autumn leaves with the wind.

It is an appealing idea for many people, to disappear for a while into a place that is totally private, isolated, and protected. Could you imagine such a place for yourself? Have you ever wanted to have a place to "hide away" from the world for a while?

On the lines below, describe the perfect hideaway for yourself. What would it look like inside? What would it look like from the outside? Where would such a hideout be? With what equipment and necessities would you furnish such a place? How long would you like to stay? What would you do while hiding away?

_____
_____
_____
_____
_____
_____
_____
_____
_____
_____
_____
_____
_____
_____
_____
_____
_____

7. The Diary of Anne Frank

Answers

Identifying Characters

(1) a	(6) h	(11) g	(16) a
(2) f	(7) h	(12) a	(17) i
(3) b	(8) b	(13) f	(18) h
(4) e	(9) d	(14) h	(19) j
(5) e	(10) c	(15) a	(20) b

Newspaper Article

Answers will vary. Sample news story:

AMSTERDAM—Their friends thought they had been killed. The Nazis thought they'd escaped to Switzerland. But close by, in the annex of his own spice business, Mr. Otto Frank hid his family, the Van Daan family, and a stranger, for 25 months before the Nazis found them.

"It was a nightmare at times," Mr. Frank said, in an interview just after his release from a prison camp two months ago. "We were silent for 10 hours each day. Then at night, when the workers left, we could read, talk, and relax a bit. But we all knew it would be a matter of time before they, or someone else, found us."

The hideaways eventually were discovered and transported to concentration camps across Germany. Nearly all of them died: Mrs. Frank, Margot Frank, Anne Frank, Mr. and Mrs. Van Daan, Peter Van Daan, and a Mr. Dussel, the stranger who asked for refuge.

Otto Frank, the only survivor, says he will publish the contents of his daughter Anne's diary, which was stored in the annex and overlooked by the Gestapo when the annex was raided.

Self-Analysis

Answers will vary.

Creative Writing

Answers will vary.

8. THE TIME MACHINE

Author: H. G. Wells
Novel Title: *The Time Machine*
Director: George Pal

Running Time: 103 minutes
Year: 1960
Format: color

Summary

It is January 5, 1900, at a home in London, England, a little after 8:00 P.M. A group of men are sitting around a living room waiting for their host, a daring inventor named George, to arrive. Suddenly George stumbles in, ragged and beaten. The men are shocked, but more so when he tells them he's returned from the future.

George begins explaining by flashing back to New Year's Eve, 1899, when all the men had gathered to see George's time machine model. Dr. Hilliers scoffed at the invention even as he pushed the lever to begin the machine's time journey (it disappeared from the table where it had been sitting all night). The group left and George sat and began a good-bye note to his maid, Mrs. Watchett. But his friend David Filby tried to talk George out of his "confusion."

David leaves with the promise to come to dinner on Friday, and George mounts his time machine to travel into the future. He stops in 1917, during World War I, and meets David Filby's son, Jamie. David has died in the war. George leaves dumbfounded. He pushes on to 1945, where London is being bombed. He dives to his time machine and proceeds to 1966, where he meets Jamie Filby as an old man running to an air-raid shelter as the world is about to be destroyed by atomic bombs. George leaps to his machine once again, and this time moves centuries into the future to arrive in a land of paradise-like tranquility.

He sees a number of young, blond men and women lounging along a riverbank, and, upon approaching them, hears screams. A girl is drowning and no one is lifting a hand to help her. George saves the girl, Weena, and thus is introduced to the strange, quiet, Eloi people.

George asks to see their libraries, only to find ancient volumes whose pages dissolve in George's hands. The Eloi have no feelings, no government, no laws, no art. George determines to leave, but finds that his time machine has been dragged a hundred feet or so behind steel doors beneath a Sphinx-like shrine. George asks Weena about his machine, and she tells him about the Morlocks, who live beneath the earth and come out only at night. Weena shows him the "talking rings" that literally spin out tales of the past. George learns that civilization was destroyed and some of the population went below ground, while the rest stayed up in the sunshine. Somehow the Morlocks have become powerful and are breeding the Eloi like cattle.

George is climbing down into one of the air tunnels that lead to the Morlocks' stronghold in order to find his machine. A siren goes off and Weena, along with hundreds of her peers, marches mindlessly toward the Sphinx, enters through the steel doors, and disappears. George runs back down the air tunnel and fights the Morlocks. He lights a torch and burns them, but at one point he is overpowered and the Eloi respond and help free him. The Morlocks' world is essentially destroyed and the Eloi are free. George gets on his machine to go back to 1900, but is attacked by a few remaining Morlocks. He fights them off, sets his time machine to "past" mode, and returns home, beaten and weary.

In the present, the men tease George about his story. George wishes them good fortune, and after they leave, mounts his machine to travel back to the Eloi to help them build a better civilization. He has taken three books along whose titles are not revealed. His friend David Filby steps into George's workshop after George has left and sees where the time machine was dragged to a place where it would be outside the walls of the Sphinx when George arrives in the future; he'll be safely out of Morlock hands.

The maid says, "Do you think he will be back?" David says, "One cannot help but wonder. . . . He's got all the time in the world."

8. The Time Machine

Multiple Choice

1. ____ George's main interest was in (a) the past (b) the present (c) the future

2. ____ According to the film, the four dimensions are (a) length, depth, thickness, eternity (b) eternity, infinity, depth, width (c) length, width, height, infinity (d) forward/backward, left/right, up/down, time

3. ____ George says that humans are trapped in the fourth dimension. What does he mean? (a) We all must die. (b) We cannot move anywhere within the time dimension. (c) We cannot move sideways when we need to. (d) We cannot change the course of history.

4. ____ When George "proves" to the businessmen that time travel is possible, they criticize his experiments. They say: (a) "Time travel is impossible." (b) "George is nuts." (c) "What use would such a machine be?" (d) "The future is irrevocable [unchangeable]!" (e) both a and b (f) all of the above (g) a, c, and d (h) none of the above

5. ____ What three different "futures" does George visit before ending up in Eloi Land? (a) 1910, 1911, 1966 (b) 1922, 1941, 1991 (c) 1917, 1940, 1966 (d) 1901, 2001, 2010

6. ____ How are George and the mannequin that he keeps seeing on his travels through time alike? (a) Neither one looks older. (b) Both are wooden-headed. (c) Both are models for all of us to imitate. (d) Both wear modern clothing.

7. ____ When George meets the Eloi people for the first time he is astounded because: (a) They're all blond. (b) They're stupid. (c) They're constantly singing country and western songs. (d) They're munching fruit while a woman is drowning.

8. ____ When George finds a library full of rotting books he is furious because: (a) The Eloi should have built a roof over them. (b) They're all overdue. (c) The Eloi have not continued man's struggle to learn. (d) The Eloi people hate him.

9. ____ From listening to the "magic rings" George learns that the Morlocks are: (a) former teachers of the Eloi (b) former used-car salesmen from the '50's (c) a strange race of people that has evolved from papaya plants (d) people who went underground during an atomic holocaust centuries before (e) both a and d (f) all of the above

8. The Time Machine

Plot Sequence

Everything happens within the framework of time. In stories things usually happen is what is called "chronological order." First things first, second things second, and so forth. (*Chronos* is the Greek word for "time.")

Below are fifteen events that make up the plot of the movie *The Time Machine*. Study them, then put them in their correct chronological order by placing the letter of the first event in the first box below, the letter of the second event in the second box, the letter of the third event in the third box, and so forth, until all the boxes are lettered. The first one is done for you.

1. ☐ f

2. ☐

3. ☐

4. ☐

5. ☐

6. ☐

7. ☐

8. ☐

9. ☐

10. ☐

11. ☐

12. ☐

13. ☐

14. ☐

15. ☐

a. The miniature time machine disappears.

b. Weena walks into the Sphinx.

c. George says good-bye to Filby for the last time.

d. George saves Weena from drowning.

e. The Morlocks try to knock George off his time machine.

f. The Doctor flicks the switch on the model time machine.

g. George meets Jamie Filby when Jamie is a young man in 1917.

h. George finds a library full of rotted books.

i. George meets Jamie Filby when Jamie is old.

j. George has the Eloi throw dead wood down the tower holes to burn up the Morlocks.

k. George lights a torch and shoves it in the Morlocks' faces.

l. A young Morlock saves George's life.

m. George pulls his time machine out from the boundaries of the Sphinx, where he left it when he returned to his present century.

n. George is trapped beneath a mountain and must wait centuries for the mountain to erode so he can get out.

o. George watches a Morlock decompose into a pile of bones.

8. The Time Machine

Verb Tense

George could go forward or backward in time on his time machine, but could never be in two time dimensions at once.

You have the same limitation when you write sentences. Each one is a "time machine" that keeps readers in the present, or sends them back to the past, or sends them forward into the future. But in no way can a reader exist in two time dimensions in the same instant.

For example, it is incorrect to say, "George ran into the woods and saves Weena from the Morlocks." The verb "ran" is past tense and the verb "saves" is present tense. This kind of writing creates a time warp in readers' minds and gives them headaches brought on by confusion.

The sentences below are time warped. Rewrite them on the lines provided so that the verbs are in the *same* time frame: past, present, or future, not two time dimensions at once.

1. George wanted to convince his friends of the reality of time travel, so he invents a time machine.

_____

_____

_____

2. George got disgusted with the doubts of his friends and leaves for the future.

_____

_____

3. He traveled ahead to 1917 then stops the machine and gets out.

_____

_____

4. He meets Jamie Filby and said, "Good-bye, Jamie."

_____

_____

5. He then traveled on to 1966 and meets Jamie, an old man who warns him of the "mushrooms."

_____

_____

6. George got back on his machine, goes far into the future, and meets the Eloi people.

_____

_____

7. He first sees Weena when he saved her from drowning.

_____

_____

8. George was astounded by the Eloi, who eat and drink and sleep and do no work.

_____

_____

8. The Time Machine

Essay Topics

Read the suggested essay topics listed below. Choose one that interests you and write a two-page essay on that subject. Remember to have an interesting introduction, body paragraphs that include many details and examples, and a conclusion that leaves no one in doubt as to your opinion.

1. George returns from the land of the Eloi to find his friends doubting him, so he decides to return. He tells Filby good-bye, then mounts his time machine and leaves, but not before taking some valuable items with him: three books. Which three books were they? Why do you think it was these three particular volumes? In your view, what value does each one have? Of what use will they be to the Eloi—or to George? Would you have taken books, or three completely different items? Why?

2. H. G. Wells, the author of the novel *The Time Machine*, seems to be saying that to be fully human takes more than just food, leisure time, and a suntan. What things do you think humans really need to be "happy"? What is our purpose on Earth? How would you define happiness? Are you happy? Why or why not?

3. H. G. Wells created a story in which a man builds a machine that can take people into the fourth dimension: time. With a flick of a lever, the driver of the time machine can visit the future or the past, and return from whence he or she came. But this is fiction, of course. Or is it? Do you believe that people can travel into the past or into the future? If so, how do they actually accomplish it?

4. At one point in *The Time Machine*, the doctor says, "The future is irrevocable. It cannot be changed!" Do you agree with this? Even if you could travel into the future, could you alter things that would change the "present" when you returned to your own time dimension? Is your destiny programmed? Can you do things today that will affect the future that awaits you in the fourth dimension?

5. An entertaining movie of the 1980's, *Back to the Future*, dealt with this same concept of time travel. Compare this film with *The Time Machine*. Which film handled the subject most intelligently? Which film told the best story? Why do you think so? Explain.

8. The Time Machine

Answers

Multiple Choice

(1) c	(6) a
(2) d	(7) d
(3) b	(8) c
(4) g	(9) d
(5) c	

Plot Sequence

(1) f	(6) d	(11) j
(2) a	(7) h	(12) e
(3) g	(8) b	(13) o
(4) i	(9) k	(14) c
(5) n	(10) l	(15) m

Verb Tense

Answers will vary. Possible rewrites:

1. George . . . so he *invented* a time machine.
2. George . . . and *left* for the future.
3. He . . . then *stopped* the machine and *got* out.
4. He *met* Jamie Filby and said. . . .
5. He . . . and *met* Jamie, an old man who *warned*. . . .
6. George . . . *went* far into the future, and *met* the Eloi people.
7. He first *saw* Weena when he. . . .
8. George . . . who *ate* and *drank* and *slept* and *did* no work.

Esay Topics

Essays will vary.

9. THE OTHER SIDE OF THE MOUNTAIN

Based on the life of Jill Kenmont

Director: Larry Peerce

Running Time: 103 minutes
Year: 1975
Format: color

Summary

Jill Kenmont is a high school Olympic hopeful in downhill skiing who is paralyzed for life in an accident during an important race called the Snow Cup.

Jill is determined to walk again and ski competitively, but the doctors tell her otherwise. She will not accept their diagnosis. Her best friend, Audrey Jo Nicholson, a fellow skier who contracted polio months before Jill's final race, confronts Jill with the truth: "You have to face that you're a cripple, and work with what you've got left!"

Jill goes through months of rehabilitation in preparation for her boyfriend Buddy Werner's visit. He arrives and waits for Jill to walk to him, but she instead shows him how she has learned to lift a potato chip to her mouth, using just the muscles in her shoulders. "When are you going to walk, Jill?" Buddy asks. "I'm never going to walk," Jill replies. And with that, Buddy walks out of her life.

She falls into a deep depression, only to be lifted from despair and her hospital bed by Dick "Mad Dog" Buick, a skiing hot-shot she'd met at one of the races and whom she'd had a crush on for years. Buick runs her wheelchair out into the street, and amid a rush of traffic, tells her he's going to stick with her until she decides to stop feeling sorry for herself and get on with her life.

Buick stays at Jill's parents' ranch and works with her in the pool and takes her out for exercise and for rides in the country. He tells her he wants to marry her and build a special house with everything low to the ground so her life will be easier. She says that she wants to find something to do that will keep her from feeling so useless. Buick says, "It looks like we have the same problem." He takes her to visit the Indian reservation near the ranch and for the first time Jill gets the idea that she could be a teacher.

Dick Buick flies off for home one day in his single-engine plane, and Jill goes to the California Rehabilitation Center, where she meets a young man (nameless, in the film) who says he's going to die in a year, but who will pursue his master's degree at UCLA. He tells her to put her brain "in training" as she did her body when she skied, and go for a teaching degree.

Jill convinces the head of the school to allow her to earn a degree. Then she celebrates by calling Dick Buick to tell him she loves him and that she wants him to fly out for her birthday party.

As the family nervously waits for Dick's arrival, they get a call that Dick Buick is dead; his plane has crashed. Jill is once again thrown into despair, but she recovers and goes on to teach at the Indian school.

The film ends where it began—at the school, with Jill surrounded by elementary-aged students who are walking along beside her wheelchair asking questions and being taught by their paraplegic teacher—the woman who made a life for herself by crossing over a mountain of despair and getting to the other side.

9. The Other Side of the Mountain

Multiple Choice

Write the letter of the correct answer to each item on the line provided.

1. ____ *The Other Side of the Mountain* takes place in: (a) Idaho (b) Colorado (c) California (d) Utah

2. ____ Originally, Jill Kenmont's goal was to: (a) break the speed-skiing record (b) marry Mad Dog Buick (c) earn a position on the Olympic ski team

3. ____ Mad Dog Buick got his nickname from: (a) being reckless (b) having a hot temper (c) getting into trouble with the police (d) breaking his neck

4. ____ Jill is drawn to Dick Buick because: (a) he's handsome (b) he's rich (c) he is a good person (d) he's daring

5. ____ Jill becomes paralyzed because: (a) her right ski broke (b) she disregarded her coach's advice (c) she was going too slow (d) she didn't know the course

6. ____ Jill's friend A. J. is paralyzed because: (a) she contracted polio (b) she fell off a ski lift (c) she was racing too fast in the Snow Cup race (d) she skied off a cliff

7. ____ A. J. visits Jill in the hospital and says: (a) she has to admit she is a loser (b) she will walk again (c) she will ski again (d) she should face the fact that she's handicapped for life

8. ____ Buddy Werner breaks up with Jill because: (a) he can't take pain (b) he hasn't got enough money to pay her medical bills (c) he doesn't want to spend his life with a handicapped person (d) he knows she will marry Dick Buick

9. ____ At the California Rehabilitation Center Jill learns that: (a) to walk is possible (b) sympathy is her worst enemy (c) anyone can do anything

10. ____ Dick Buick arrives to help Jill because: (a) he cares (b) he needs the money (c) he likes difficult challenges (d) he needs some important purpose in his life (e) a and b (f) a, b, and c (g) a, b, c, and d

9. The Other Side of the Mountain

Definition Essay

When most people want a definition they go to the dictionary. But some words aren't defined so easily. The word "strength," for instance, can mean the ability to endure pain, fear, or loss. "Strength" can mean different things to different people.

Choose one of the topics below and write a *definition essay*, that is, a detailed, personal definition of one of the terms. Compare your term to things common to people so they can better understand your point. Also, you can tell what your topic does for people, how it works in everyday life, and what it is similar to and different from. Brainstorm before you write by listing ideas that quickly come to mind when you think of the topic. Then organize those thoughts into more detailed examples in order to clearly define your term.

Luck. Is there such a thing as luck? Is it a feeling? A superstition? What does luck look like or feel like? Who has luck and who doesn't?

Courage. How does courage function in a person? Is everybody courageous? Always, or only when there's trouble? Is courage found in ordinary people doing ordinary things? Or is courage found on battlefields and racetracks?

Success. Is it money? Possessions? Power? An elegant mansion, an exclusive school, a place in the starting lineup, a picture on the cover of a national magazine? How do we know when we've succeeded or failed?

Freedom. Is it the chance to choose? To do whatever you want whenever you want? Is it political? Spiritual? Social? Does freedom depend on the amount of power you have? Does it depend on the amount of military power you have? Can anybody be free, anywhere on earth? How?

Friend. What is a friend? (What is an enemy?) What qualities does a friend possess? Do you have to earn a friend's companionship? How do you keep a friend? How can you lose one?

Love. Can you see "love"? Can you learn it at school? Can it be bought, traded, earned, created, discovered, cheapened, lost? Can you learn "love" like you learn geography or math? How does love happen in the real world?

Teacher. What is a teacher? Who can teach? Can you learn to do it? Is it an art or a science? Is everybody a teacher in some ways? Are some people "born teachers"?

9. The Other Side of the Mountain

Poetry

Below is a poem by the great American writer Emily Dickinson. Read the poem, then think about the questions asked below. Don't answer each question separately; combine your answers into a brief essay that sums up how you think Jill Kenmont's life paralleled the experience of Dickinson. If you wish to expand your answer, write on the back of the page.

MY LIFE CLOSED TWICE

My life closed twice before its close;
It yet remains to see
If immortality unveil
A third event to me,

So huge, so hopeless to conceive,
As these that twice befell.
Parting is all we know of Heaven,
And all we need of Hell.

- What were the two "closings" in Jill Kenmont's life?
- What happened to Jill after these tragic "closings"?
- What other doors opened up after these tragedies?
- What does Dickinson mean in the last two lines of the poem?
- Is she right? Would Jill agree with her?
- Who seems to be more hopeful, Emily Dickinson or Jill Kenmont? Why? Explain.

9. The Other Side of the Mountain

Spelling Puzzle

When the movie begins, Jill Kenmont is teaching Indian children how to spell "spear." One child spells "S-P-E-E-R"—a common mistake. Below are 15 other words taken from the movie that are misspelled here. With a partner, determine the correct spelling for each word, then circle the correctly spelled version in the "search box."

Misspelled Words

skeeing	frend	paralised
airplain	Olimpicks	trajedy
kwalify	romanse	acident
carear	hospitle	recuvery
teecher	mountin	athleet

```
s  k  i  i  n  g  g  b  e  e  p  v  i  e  r
f  t  a  g  h  i  e  r  t  y  a  b  b  l  e
r  c  e  b  n  m  k  j  h  g  r  q  u  a  c
i  o  b  a  b  n  q  n  q  u  a  l  i  f  y
e  h  m  a  c  h  a  c  c  i  l  e  n  t  e
n  b  c  a  r  h  f  f  c  h  y  r  e  c  o
d  m  e  n  n  b  e  q  u  a  z  p  p  y  c
a  m  z  i  e  c  a  r  l  e  e  d  o  o  r
i  b  c  a  r  e  e  r  a  t  d  h  e  l  e
r  u  a  t  k  c  m  o  u  n  t  a  i  n  c
p  k  c  h  l  e  h  l  n  p  o  i  y  u  o
l  b  c  l  h  c  k  y  m  p  v  u  x  z  v
a  a  i  e  t  r  r  m  o  u  n  t  l  e  e
n  q  d  t  h  o  s  p  i  t  a  l  l  a  r
e  w  e  e  t  r  a  i  t  r  a  g  e  d  y
s  a  n  p  l  r  s  c  b  v  n  i  e  d  y
w  e  t  e  l  l  y  s  a  t  m  i  n  z  p
```

9. The Other Side of the Mountain

Answers

Multiple Choice

(1) c   (2) c   (3) a   (4) c   (5) b   (6) a   (7) d   (8) c   (9) b   (10) g

Definition Essay

Essays will vary.

Poetry

Sample:

Jill's life, like Dickinson's, did close twice—first when she was paralyzed and could no longer follow her championship dream, and then, when Dick Buick died in a plane crash. Jill struggled and prevailed over both of these tragedies and went on with her life. She got her degree and taught at the Indian school as she and Dick had planned. Her courage paid off, and served as a model for others who have suffered great loss.

Dickinson's poem captures much of what Jill Kenmont's life was, especially the last two lines. Jill knew what it was to part from things forever. And it hurt. Dickinson implies that the torment of hell itself cannot be worse than saying good-bye to someone you love. Jill Kenmont might readily agree, but she would also say that life is a gift, and through courage and hard work, a person can still lead a bountiful, fulfilling life.

Spelling Puzzle

Misspelled words:

skeeing—skiing
frend—friend
airplain—airplane
Olimpicks—Olympics
kwalify—qualify
romanse—romance
acident—accident
paralised—paralyzed
teecher—teacher
trajedy—tragedy
mountin—mountain
athleet—athelete
carear—career
hospitle—hospital
recuvery—recovery

10. A Christmas Carol

The version used in this text was a made-for-television movie starring George C. Scott. The film was sponsored by IBM, and it is shown each year during the month of December. Have students watch the movie and do the activities as an at-home assignment.

Summary

The movie opens with the miser Ebenezer Scrooge doing shrewd business at the stock exchange. He is surly and ungenerous with his clerk, Bob Cratchit. He is asked by two men to give a donation to help the poor and needy at Christmastime. Scrooge's reply is, "If they'd rather die, perhaps they'd better do so, and decrease the surplus population."

This attitude "haunts" Scrooge throughout the movie, in the persons of three spirits—Christmas Past, Christmas Present, and Christmas Future—who are introduced to Scrooge by the ghost of his deceased business partner, Jacob Marley. Marley, wrapped in chains and money boxes, appears and says, "I have come for your sake, Ebenezer," and proceeds to warn Scrooge of three soon-to-arrive spirits.

At 1 A.M., the Spirit of Christmas Past appears. She shows Scrooge his bitter, lonely childhood, lightened only by the presence of his beloved sister, Fran, and a beautiful girl named Belle, whom he rejected in favor of business pursuits. At 2 A.M., the Spirit of Christmas Present arrives and shows Scrooge how the Cratchits and Scrooge's nephew, Fred, are celebrating the day. Then the spirit takes Scrooge to the edge of London, where poor families are gathered over open fires in the cold.

He opens his robe and shows him two starved, dirty children whose names are Ignorance and Want. Scrooge cowers from the sight and begs to go home. But his request is met by the third spirit, who arrives in a black robe and who is gruesome and terribly frightening (the Grim Reaper, we assume). He leads Scrooge to a cemetery where the shivering miser stoops and sweeps the snow off a gravestone upon which his name is inscribed: Ebenezer Scrooge. Scrooge weeps and tries to convince the spirit that this can be changed, that he can mend his ways and avoid a lonely, despicable death.

The spirit does not answer. Scrooge falls on the stone, then suddenly wakes in bed with the realization that it is Christmas morning, and that he can indeed change his ways and attitudes toward his fellow human beings. He immediately sends the Cratchits a huge turkey, then visits his nephew, Fred, and apologizes for saying and believing that Christmas was a "humbug."

In the final scene, Scrooge embraces Bob Cratchit, doubles his salary, and promises to help his crippled son Tiny Tim recover: "Tim will walk again!" he says. And with that the narrator tells us that Scrooge was considered a man who "kept Christmas well." And the film ends.

10. A Christmas Carol

Multiple Choice

Write the letter of the correct answer to the questions below on the line provided.

1. ____ Jacob Marley was: (a) Scrooge's nephew (b) Scrooge's boss (c) Scrooge's partner (d) Scrooge's employee

2. ____ Marley's ghost tells Scrooge that: (a) his (Marley's) ghost is condemned to roam the earth doing what it should have done in life (b) kindness should have been his business when he was alive (c) the chain he wears he forged in life by being selfish (d) he has come to warn Ebenezer of the dangers of a selfish life (e) both a and b (f) none of the above (g) a, b, c, and d

3. ____ The first two spirits each remind Scrooge that: (a) he will die alone and unloved (b) he was disliked by his father (c) his nephew, Fred, looks very much like his sister, Fran

4. ____ The second spirit is (a) the Spirit of Christmas Past (b) the Spirit of Christmas Eve (c) the Spirit of New Year's (d) the Spirit of Christmas Present (e) none of the above

5. ____ The first spirit shows Scrooge some people who were important to him during childhood and youth. They are: (a) Bob Cratchit, Belle, and Old Fezziwig (b) Belle, Fran, and Scrooge's father (c) Old Fezziwig, Scrooge's father, and Fred (d) Fred, Fran, and Belle

6. ____ The Spirit of Christmas Past shows Scrooge that he could have had: (a) a loving family and a good marriage (b) a healthy relationship with his father (c) a better career

7. ____ Scrooge refused to pull the sheet off a corpse because it was: (a) his friend, Marley (b) Tiny Tim (c) his dead sister (d) Belle (e) himself (f) Bob Cratchit

8. ____ At the opening of the movie, Scrooge's greatest fear was: (a) being late for the exchange (b) paying Bob Cratchit more money (c) having to give anything to others (d) being called a tightwad (e) none of the above

9. ____ At the end of the movie Scrooge's greatest fear was: (a) dying alone and unloved (b) being late for the exchange (c) waiting for the third spirit (d) helping Tiny Tim and his family

10. A Christmas Carol

Quiz

Section A. Matching
Draw a line connecting each character with the phrase that best describes him or her.

1. Marley   realizes that life is more than money

2. Scrooge   points the black finger of death

3. Bob Cratchit   narrates the opening and closing of the film

4. Tiny Tim   all tied up with money boxes

5. Mrs. Cratchit   hates Mr. Scrooge

6. Spirit of Christmas Past   shows Scrooge what he is missing

7. Spirit of Christmas Present   shows Scrooge where he went wrong

8. Spirit of Christmas Future   loved Ebenezer very much when he was a boy

9. Fran   His whole life is his family.

10. Fred   believes someday he will walk again

Section B. True or False
Put "+" next to the true statements and a zero (0) next to the false statements.

1. ___ *A Christmas Carol* is about how happiness and kindness are worth more than riches.
2. ___ One of Charles Dickens's themes in *A Christmas Carol* is that money should be used for the benefit of everyone.
3. ___ The climax of the story is when the Spirit of Christmas Present pulls back his robe to reveal two starving children.
4. ___ The three Spirits of Christmas came to help Ebenezer.
5. ___ Marley's ghost comes to threaten Ebenezer Scrooge with death.
6. ___ As a boy, Scrooge lived with his grandmother, who loved him.
7. ___ Each spirit that appears is more stern and threatening than the one before.
8. ___ Fred's goal in life is to become his uncle Scrooge's business partner.
9. ___ When Scrooge realizes that no one will miss him when he dies because he has been so selfish, he changes his attitude toward life.
10. ___ Bob Cratchit is a heroic character who believes in the power of love.

10. A Christmas Carol

Similes

A simile is a comparison using the words *like* or *as*. Its purpose is to make an idea, action, emotion, or physical image clear to the reader. For instance, if you saw a beautiful full moon on a cold autumn night, you might describe the image as follows:

The moon was like a silver coin on a black velvet cloak.

Below are several similes in which only half the comparison is given. Provide the other half of each simile by creating something unique for comparison. Instead of "black as night" (which is very common and over-used), you might say, "black as a panther's eyes."

1. as black as

   _____

2. as sharp as

   _____

3. as big as

   _____

4. as blue as

   _____

5. as mean as

   _____

6. as strong as

   _____

7. as tight as

   _____

8. as soft as

   _____

9. as old as

   _____

10. as cute as

    _____

Create more of your own similes below:

11. The wind howled like _____

    _____

12. Scrooge danced like _____

    _____

13. Marley's ghost sailed out the window

    as if _____

    _____

14. The children shivered in the cold like

    _____

15. Bob Cratchit snuck into Scrooge's shop

    like _____

16. The fog was as thick as _____

    _____

17. The Spirit of Christmas Present

    laughed like _____

18. Getting a prize turkey for Christmas

    dinner was like _____

19. At first, Scrooge's heart was as cold as

    _____

20. Losing Tiny Tim would be like

    _____

10. A Christmas Carol

Vocabulary

Below are ten words used in the movie *A Christmas Carol*. Draw a line from each word to its definition, located in the right-hand column; then, at the bottom of the page, write a paragraph about the movie, using *all ten words*.

1. penance	unpredictable
2. anonymous	name unknown
3. fetter	self-restraint
4. apparition	one who hordes money
5. miser	disgusting
6. odious	chain
7. mercurial	kindness
8. benevolence	all-inclusive; complete
9. forbearance	ghost
10. comprehensive	making up for a sin or crime

Paragraph

_____

_____

_____

_____

_____

_____

_____

_____

_____

_____

10. A Christmas Carol

Answers

Multiple Choice

(1) c　(2) g　(3) c　(4) d　(5) b　(6) a　(7) e　(8) c　(9) a

Quiz

Section A. Matching

   (1) Marley—all tied up with money boxes
   (2) Scrooge—realizes that life is more than money
   (3) Bob Cratchit—his whole life is his family
   (4) Tiny Tim—believes someday he will walk again
   (5) Mrs. Cratchit—hates Mr. Scrooge
   (6) Spirit of Christmas Past—shows Scrooge where he went wrong
   (7) Spirit of Christmas Present—shows Scrooge what he is missing
   (8) Spirit of Christmas Future—points the black finger of death
   (9) Fran—loved Ebenezer very much when he was a boy
  (10) Fred—narrates the opening and closing of the film

Section B. True or False

   (1) +　(2) +　(3) 0　(4) +　(5) 0　(6) 0　(7) +　(8) 0　(9) +　(10) +

Similes

Samples:

   (1) as black as *used motor oil*
   (2) as sharp as *new scissors*
   (3) as big as *Texas*
   (4) as blue as *a mountain lake*
   (5) as mean as *a badger*
   (6) as strong as *a bulldozer*
   (7) as tight as *a tourniquet*
   (8) as soft as *duck fluff*
   (9) as old as *a star*
  (10) as cute as *a baby duck*

  (11) *. . . a lost child*
  (12) *. . . a marionette*
  (13) *he were a scrap of paper*
  (14) *fluttering oak leaves*
  (15) *a prowler*
  (16) *a velvet curtain*
  (17) *a wild man*
  (18) *winning the lottery*
  (19) *the dark side of the moon*
  (20) *brutal torture*

Vocabulary

   (1) penance—making up for a sin or crime
   (2) anonymous—name unknown
   (3) fetter—chain
   (4) apparition—ghost
   (5) miser—one who hordes money
   (6) odious—disgusting
   (7) mercurial—unpredictable
   (8) benevolence—kindness
   (9) forbearance—self-restraint
  (10) comprehensive—all-inclusive

Paragraph:　Answers will vary.

11. BERNICE BOBS HER HAIR

Author: William Faulkner
Short Story Title: "Bernice Bobs Her Hair"
Director: Peter Werner

Running Time: 49 minutes
Year: 1980
Format: color

Summary

Bernice is a college-aged girl from Eau Claire, Wisconsin, who is visiting her cousin, Marjorie, for part of the summer. She is timid, crooked-toothed, and Victorian in manner and thought, especially when it comes to members of the opposite sex. Marjorie, on the other hand, is a worldly, dark-haired expert in the art of attracting boys.

The movie opens at a dance where a boy named Otis has been assigned to Bernice as a dance partner, but is losing interest in the whole proposition. Marjorie is called upon to rescue Otis, and she does—by assigning her former boyfriend, Warren MacIntyre, to the job. Warren fusses, but accepts the chore of entertaining Bernice, who now refuses to dance. She talks about the weather and such, until Warren says that she has a very kissable mouth.

Bernice says, "Fresh!" And that's the end of her conversation with her escort.

That night Marjorie tells her mother, "She's ruining my whole summer!" Bernice overhears and confronts Marjorie the following day. Marjorie tells Bernice that she ought to leave if she's so unhappy.

But Bernice does the opposite; she gives herself over to the instruction of her cousin, who promises to make Bernice into someone who will interest boys. Marjorie tells Bernice to smile like the Mona Lisa to hide her crooked teeth and to say witty, interesting things that will spark conversation with the boys.

Bernice takes this advice to heart, and the next social gathering, a dinner at Marjorie's, starts with a bang. Bernice announces she will get her hair "bobbed" at the first opportunity. Everyone is excited at the possibility, especially the boys and especially Warren, who suddenly sees Bernice as a daring young woman with an adventurous spirit. He shifts his affections from Marjorie to Bernice and in the process sets the girls at odds.

At a picnic, Marjorie prods Bernice into following through on her promise to "bob" (cut off) her hair. In the presence of the group Bernice can hardly refuse, and from that moment the tone of the movie changes. Bernice sits bravely in the barber's chair while her golden locks fall to the floor in bunches. The bystanders, including Marjorie, are stunned by the seriousness of the occasion and sadly watch a very pleasant girl sacrifice her looks to the cause of "being accepted." That night, Bernice tells Marjorie, "I've already gotten used to it."

After midnight, Bernice packs her things, and in a moment of clear-headed revenge, chops Marjorie's pigtails off and tosses them triumphantly into the back seat of the family car as she walks toward the train station and toward the trouble facing her back home in Eau Claire. What made her acceptable in her cousin's world will cause rejection back home, but somehow we feel that Bernice won't mind. In fact, we get the impression that she will be able to handle herself quite well, and maintain her integrity while seeking adventurous conversation with the male population in her own small town, where ". . . there's always a breeze, even on the hottest days."

11. Bernice Bobs Her Hair

Short Answers

Write a complete sentence that answers each question on the lines provided.

1. What does Marjorie try to talk Warren into doing in the first scene?

   _____

2. What is Warren upset about?

   _____

3. When Warren asks Bernice to dance, what does she say?

   _____

4. What is Warren's "line" that he uses when talking to Bernice?

   _____

5. What does Bernice accidentally overhear outside Marjorie's door?

   _____

6. What happened that made Bernice want to change her ways?

   _____

7. What does Marjorie try to teach Bernice?

   _____

8. What are the only "three topics of conversation" that should come up when a girl talks to a boy, according to Marjorie?

   _____

   _____

9. What does Marjorie "push" Bernice into doing?

   _____

10. What is Bernice's revenge?

   _____

   _____

11. Bernice Bobs Her Hair

Vocabulary

At the right is a list of words and definitions that either were used in the movie or refer to the events and time period of *Bernice Bobs Her Hair*. Study the list, then compose a newspaper column for the Society Page, using all the vocabulary words to tell of Bernice's visit with her cousin Marjorie. Be sure to include details of the party at which Bernice was such a hit. And don't forget the last daring act of this once-timid young lady that astounds everyone, including her cousin Marjorie.

coy—pretending to be shy

coquette—a female flirt

fresh—bold, rude

vivacious—full of life, lively

bob—to cut hair short

amoral—without moral sense

beau—boyfriend

vain—conceited

Bernice: The Girl Is a Sheer Genius!

_____   _____
_____   _____
_____   _____
_____   _____
_____   _____
_____   _____
_____   _____
_____   _____
_____   _____
_____   _____
_____   _____

11. Bernice Bobs Her Hair

Personal Notes

Have you ever been dared to do something, and done it? Ever had that sinking feeling when you checked in a mirror after a haircut? Ever felt like a stick-in-the-mud at a party? Ever felt out of place while staying at someone's home?

On the lines below, tell about how you got into each type of situation—how you felt before and afterward, and how you were changed because of the experience. If none of these experiences are part of your life, then write in one of your own and tell about it.

1. Tell about a time when you were dared to do something. What happened? How did you feel?

   _____

   _____

   _____

2. Tell about a time when you visited a friend or relative and found that you were "out of place" or even unwelcome. What happened? How did you feel? Did it change your relationship with your friend or relative?

   _____

   _____

   _____

3. Tell about when you were at a dance or other social gathering and you felt left out. What happened? What did you decide about attending more of the same kinds of gatherings?

   _____

   _____

   _____

4. Tell about the worst haircut or hairdo of your life. What happened? How did you feel?

   _____

   _____

   _____

11. Bernice Bobs Her Hair

Comparison

The subjects listed below are important to young people no matter which decade of the modern age they come from. List the differences between how Bernice and her friends dealt with each subject and how young people today deal with the same thing. How are things different? And in what ways are things amazingly the same?

1920's	TODAY
meeting girls/boys for the first time	meeting girls/boys for the first time
being popular	being popular
handling peer pressure	handling peer pressure
being a confident, independent person	being a confident, independent person

11. Bernice Bobs Her Hair

Answers

Short Answers

1. She tries to talk Warren into dancing with Bernice.

2. He came to dance with Marjorie but hasn't been able to.

3. It's too warm to dance.

4. "You have an awfully kissable mouth."

5. Marjorie is telling her mother how Bernice is ruining the summer vacation.

6. A boy comes calling and says that he couldn't imagine Bernice dancing.

7. She tries to teach Bernice how to make herself attractive to boys.

8. The only three topics should be you, me, and us.

9. She pushes Bernice into getting her hair "bobbed."

10. Bernice cuts Marjorie's braids and tosses them onto the car seat on her way out.

Vocabulary

Sample:

> Without being *vain*, without being *fresh*, a girl has come to town and stolen the heart of many a *beau* in the community. Her name is Bernice. She is *vivacious* without being a *coquette*. She is *coy* without being *amoral*. Her reputation has been built on the bold announcement that she will *bob* her hair before the summer is out. Let's wait and see if this girl has as much grit as she has daring!

Personal Notes

Answers will vary.

Comparison

1920's:

> *meeting boys/girls for the first time*: very shy; usually in the parlor of the girl's home; girls weren't to make the first bit of conversation.
> *being popular*: riding in an open car; appearing to be dashing and bold in doing things like a girl's wearing clothes that exposed her knees; cutting off one's long hair.
> *handling peer pressure*: If one was to be accepted in the "in" crowd, one had to do what appeared to be shocking in the eyes of adults and peers alike.
> *being a confident, independent person*: People had to act out of their own convictions and beliefs, ignoring the taunts of others to "come along and join the party."

Today: Answers will vary.

12. THE AUTOBIOGRAPHY OF MISS JANE PITTMAN

Author: Ernest J. Gaines
Novel Title: *The Autobiography of Miss Jane Pittman*
Director: John Korty

Running Time: 110 minutes
Year: 1974
Format: color

Summary

The story of Jane Pittman, 110-year-old ex-slave, is told within the framework of an interview by a young white man who drives to Louisiana in February of 1962 to hear whatever Jane Pittman has to say. He doesn't arrive, however, until a black youth named Jimmy stops by to enlist Miss Jane in the civil rights action that they are planning at the courthouse in Bayonne. Jane does not go, and says she'll wait for a sign from God before she gets involved. The viewer learns that this comment is a foreshadowing of hard things to come for Jane Pittman.

The young reporter arrives and Jane recalls the events of her life.

She was freed in 1863 and departed with a group of men, women, and children who left just hours after hearing the Emancipation Proclamation read by their former owner from the front porch of his mansion. She was headed for Ohio because a soldier named Lewis Brown who gave her the name "Jane" lived there, and it was the only place she'd heard of that was officially in the North.

On the journey with her fellow freed slaves, the "patrollers" catch up with them and murder everyone but Jane and a boy named Ned. She gathers a piece of iron and a flint rock and hands them to Ned. "Take care of these. Make sure they get to Ohio the same time we do," she says.

She never makes it to Ohio in her lifetime. The struggle for food, shelter, and water drives her to sign on at the Dye plantation for 12 years. There Ned is harassed by the Ku Klux Klan and is forced to leave for Kansas. Jane stays. She meets Joe Pittman, a horseman who breaks wild mustangs, and marries him. They sell everything they have to pay the wicked Colonel Dye fifty dollars "Klux money" and walk to east Texas, where Joe has a job breaking horses at the Clyde Ranch.

In Texas Jane has a good life, but it is short-lived. An albino mustang appears one day in a shipment of horses and Jane senses that it is an evil creature. She lets the horse loose; Joe runs it down and is killed. The horse returns, dragging her beloved by a rope.

Years later, Jane is back in Louisiana, living alone, when Ned shows up. He preaches equality and dignity to his black neighbors. He gives a powerful speech about what it is to be a "man" and not a "nigger," then says to Jane, "Momma, I'm gonna die." He is murdered soon after by a shotgun-wielding killer, Albert Cluveaux, who is a neighbor of Jane's and a hired hand of the Klan.

The story shifts, in its final scenes, to 1962, where there are riots in the streets and arrests of "black agitators." Jimmy, her best friend Lena's son, has been selected as "the one" who will lead his people to a measure of freedom. He plans to resist the white power structure by having a young girl drink from the "white folks's fountain" so she'll be arrested and the group can then march on the courthouse in protest. They want Jane along. Her dignity will bring the "multitudes." Jane does not go. The girl is arrested but Jimmy is killed.

The film ends with Jane drinking from the "whites-only" fountain and being followed out of town by a long line of black people who have watched this old woman make the first move against racism, using her age and her dignity to strike the blow.

12. The Autobiography of Miss Jane Pittman

Quiz

True or False

Mark the true statements below with a plus (+) and the false statements with a zero (0).

1. _____ Jane Pittman was born a slave.

2. _____ Jane Pittman was raised in the South but was educated in the North.

3. _____ Jane's dream as a teenager was to get to Ohio.

4. _____ Jane led the slaves out of the South immediately after they were set free.

5. _____ Jane never made it to the North as she had intended.

6. _____ Albert Cluveaux was a member of the Ku Klux Klan.

7. _____ Ned taught the black people that the whites were not to be trusted.

8. _____ Ned preached that all blacks should move to Africa and form their own nation.

9. _____ Ned was killed in Bayonne by police during a demonstration.

10. _____ Jimmy was called "the one" by the older black people in the community.

Matching

Match the characters listed on the left with the descriptions on the right by writing the corresponding number on the lines. (Some characters will have more than one description listed.)

1. Ned   ___ killed in Bayonne

2. Jimmy   ___ killed on the Clyde Ranch

3. Jane   ___ killed by patrollers

4. Big Laura   ___ murdered on the road

5. Albert Cluveaux   ___ originally named "Ticey"

6. Colonel Dye   ___ a hired killer

7. Joe Pittman   ___ a genius with horses

                        ___ protested segregation at age 110

                        ___ charged Joe Pittman fifty dollars to leave his plantation

                        ___ broke the law by drinking at a "whites-only" fountain

12. The Autobiography of
Miss Jane Pittman

Past and Future

Jane Pittman lived 110 years, from 1852 to 1962. During her lifetime the world changed drastically in many different areas: technology, education, business, etc. Take a moment to list some of those changes on the lines in the left column. Then, in the right column, list some changes that you think will occur by the time you reach your 110th birthday.

During Jane's Lifetime	In the Future
Technology _____	Technology _____
_____	_____
_____	_____
Education _____	Education _____
_____	_____
_____	_____
Business _____	Business _____
_____	_____
_____	_____
Law _____	Law _____
_____	_____
_____	_____
Politics _____	Politics _____
_____	_____
_____	_____
Science _____	Science _____
_____	_____
_____	_____
Music _____	Music _____
_____	_____
_____	_____
Art _____	Art _____
_____	_____
_____	_____

12. The Autobiography of Miss Jane Pittman

Plot Construction

The plot of a story is built around the decisions and choices of the main character(s). In *The Autobiography of Miss Jane Pittman*, Jane makes many decisions that changed the path her life would take. Below is a "plot tree" with numerous "branches" that represent the different choices Jane made. At each "Y" in the upper half of the plot tree, briefly note the decision Jane made which led to the next juncture, or point of decision. (Ignore the gray, lower portion of the plot tree.)

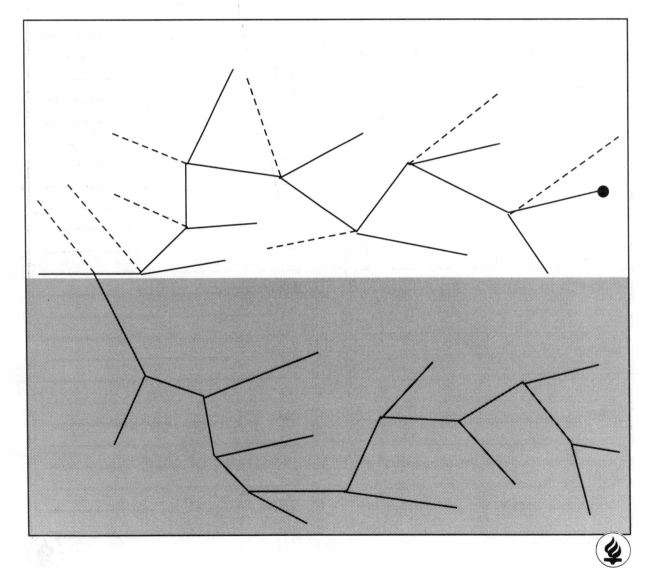

12. The Autobiography of Miss Jane Pittman

Plot Possibilities

Below is a plot tree with "branches." Every "Y" in the branch network marks a point where a decision was made. The lower half of this tree can represents *what could have been*. Imagine what Jane Pittman's life would have been like if she had chosen to *stay* on the plantation instead of heading north to Ohio. At every "Y" in the lower half, note what decision she might have made. Inside the small box, tell how her "other" life would have turned out.

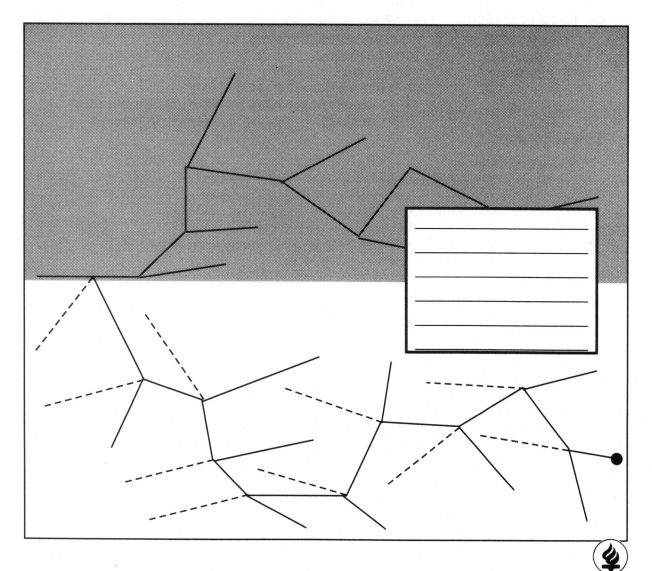

12. The Autobiography of Miss Jane Pittman

Answers

Quiz

True or False

(1) +　(2) 0　(3) +　(4) 0　(5) +　(6) +　(7) 0　(8) 0　(9) 0　(10) +

Matching

1. Ned	2—killed in Bayonne
2. Jimmy	6—killed on the Clyde Ranch
3. Jane	4—killed by patrollers
4. Big Laura	1—murdered on the road
5. Albert Cluveaux	3—originally named "Ticey"
6. Colonel Dye	5—a hired killer
7. Joe Pittman	7—a genius with horses
	3—protested segregation at age 110
	6—charged Joe Pittman fifty dollars to leave his plantation
	3—broke the law by drinking at a "whites-only" fountain

Past and Future

During Jane's Lifetime

Technology—cars, television, telephones, computers, radios, medicines

Education—black colleges, black professionals in all fields of endeavor

Business—blacks running their own companies; equal opportunity employers

Law—equal opportunity laws set by federal government

Politics—Civil Rights Act of 1964; many black mayors and a governor in the U.S.

Science—black scientists are at every major university

Music—great jazz musicians, singers; modern artists have their own albums and recording companies

Art—famous black actors, writers (like Ernest Gaines), dancers, and poets (e.g., Langston Hughes)

In the Future

Answers will vary.

Plot Construction

(1) Decides to go north. (2) Decides to take Ned with her. (3) Decides to hire on at the Dye Plantation. (4) Sends Ned away to a "safe" state. (5) Marries Joe Pittman. (6) Moves to the Clyde Ranch in Texas. (7) Consults fortune teller, then sets white horse free. (8) Moves to Louisiana. (9) Decides to go to Bayonne and drink from fountain. (10) Rides out of town to finish her life at the plantation.

Plot Possibilities

Answers will vary.

13. BORN FREE

Author: Joy Adamson
Book Title: *Born Free*
Director: James Hill

Running Time: 90 minutes
Year: 1965
Format: color

Summary

Born Free is based on a true story about accomplishing the impossible—training a tame lion to become wild and to live successfully among its own kind.

Joy Adamson, English wife of the senior game warden for the northern Kenya District of Africa, is presented with lion cub triplets by her husband, George, after he has shot the cubs' mother during a hunt for a man-eating lion (depicted in the opening scene). Joy warms to all three babies, but especially takes to the smallest, most curious, whom Joy names Elsa after a small, intelligent girl she once knew and liked.

Joy tames Elsa, with the help and enthusiasm of George and Nuru, her Kenyan housekeeper. Elsa accompanies them on trips, plays catch, and does a poor job as a "watch-cat" for the Adamsons.

Trouble begins when Elsa starts roaming and getting into the sights of hunters who don't know she's someone's pet. Then she makes serious trouble by chasing a herd of elephants, which she considers her friendly chase-mates, through a village. This results in the head ranger, John Kendall, placing an ultimatum before the Adamsons: Elsa must either go to a zoo, or be killed. Joy is strongly against a zoo, and gets Kendall's permission to try to train Elsa to go back to living wild. Kendall says it will be a waste of time, that it is impossible. But Joy and George must try, and so set out to spend the next three months "training" Elsa to live in the bush on her own.

At first Elsa fails miserably. She meets a male lion, but she is not interested in him, and jumps back onto her perch atop the roof of the Land Rover. Then she runs down a warthog, and in a very funny scene, is battered about by this tiny pig, till George and Joy are completely embarrassed. George and Joy leave her overnight, then out alone for a week, but Elsa returns, beaten and bleeding and starving. George argues with Joy about the torture they're putting Elsa through: "What's wrong with a zoo?" George demands. Joy declares that Elsa must live free and that they must continue to help her.

Finally, with two weeks left of the three-month deadline, Joy and George release Elsa, when she is "in season," and they watch Elsa fight a female lion. Joy fires a gun to end the fight because she can't stand to see Elsa suffer. Elsa then turns and walks off into the wild. George says, "You can be proud of what you did. Elsa is free now."

"I am proud—of her," Joy replies.

A year later, after their governmental required leave, they return to check up on Elsa. On the last day of their week-long search, Elsa shows up with three cubs. The reunion is emotional for the Adamsons and they are proud of what this lion has been able to do—the impossible. Joy wants to pick up one of Elsa's cubs, then says, "But I knew better now. . . ."

The movie ends with Elsa returning to the bush with her three cubs in tow, while her mate roars from a rock above the camp.

"We saw her many times," narrates Joy Adamson, "born free and living free, but to us she was always the same, our friend, Elsa."

13. Born Free

True or False and Why?

Mark the true statements below with a plus (+) and the false statements with a zero (0). Then, on the lines provided, tell exactly *why* the false statements are untrue.

1. ____ George shot and killed Elsa's mother.

   _____

2. ____ Elsa's favorite pastime was chasing herds of zebras.

   _____

3. ____ Elsa's first trip into the wild wasn't glamorous, but it was successful.

   _____

4. ____ The head warden felt that the best place for Elsa was in a zoo.

   _____

5. ____ Elsa never learned to kill wild game.

   _____

6. ____ At one point Elsa was bullied and chased by a wild pig who was one fifth her size.

   _____

7. ____ George sent Elsa's siblings to the zoo, but he couldn't let Elsa go.

   _____

8. ____ Because of the conflict over Elsa's fate, Joy and George Adamson divorced and moved back to London.

   _____

9. ____ Elsa finally walked off into the wild and never returned.

   _____

10. ____ Two years after Elsa was released to live freely on the African plain, Joy Adamson adopted a baby gorilla.

   _____

13. Born Free

Short Answers

1. Why did Joy Adamson name her favorite cub Elsa?

   _____

2. Why is John Kendall, the head game warden, afraid of Elsa?

   _____

3. What "crime" does Elsa commit that forces Joy and George Adamson to "do something" with her?

   _____

   _____

4. What did Elsa have to learn before she could survive in the wild?

   _____

5. Why did George and Joy Adamson choose to live on the African plain?

   _____

6. What were some of the disadvantages in having Elsa as a pet?

   _____

7. Why do you think Joy got so attached that she wanted to "adopt" Elsa?

   _____

8. If Elsa had been the biggest cub in her family, how might the story have turned out?

   _____

   _____

9. What do you think would have happened if George had shipped Elsa off to the zoo?

   _____

10. How do you think George and Joy's relationship was affected by the experience of adopting, then releasing Elsa?

    _____

    _____

13. Born Free

Vocabulary

Below are ten vocabulary words based on the movie *Born Free*. Draw a line from each word to its definition (use a dictionary when necessary), then write a brief paragraph that tells what *Born Free* was about, using at least six of the vocabulary words.

1. menace   overjoyed
2. province   liquid infant food
3. safari   a prearranged meeting
4. formula   the act of granting freedom
5. pride   a territory
6. reserve   a group of lions
7. rendezvous   an expedition (usually for hunting)
8. precedent   a threat
9. emancipation   an example
10. ecstatic   an area of land set aside for a specific purpose

Paragraph

13. Born Free

Essay Topics

An essay tells what a person thinks about a topic or event. If a person is against eating meat because it involves killing animals, then an essay on that subject would include two things: (1) a sentence stating the author's "anti-meat-eating" opinion, and (2) a series of sentences, grouped into paragraphs, that use facts and examples to support the author's opinion.

Choose one of the topics below, based on events in the film *Born Free*. State your opinion clearly and support or "defend" your thinking with sensible facts and examples. Follow whatever guidelines your teacher sets for length and manuscript style.

1. Much of the tension in the movie *Born Free* is built around the argument that some things are simply impossible for humans to accomplish. Think of a time when you ran up against something that seemed impossible for you, but you did it anyway and succeeded. What do you think makes people try the "impossible"? What is it in humans that makes us willing to risk everything to do something that people say can't be done?

2. Some people think that cities are "human zoos." Do you agree? or disagree? Why do you feel the way you do? Explain, using lots of examples to support your opinion.

3. Lots of people have pets: dogs, cats, fish, hamsters, snakes, etc. Do you see anything wrong with keeping pets? Should Joy Adamson have tamed Elsa and kept her as a house pet? Is there a difference between making Elsa a pet, and making a hamster or a snake a pet?

4. Many people have formed organizations to defend the rights of animals. What rights do you think animals have? Or do you think they shouldn't have any? Should certain animals have some rights that others don't? What is man's responsibility to the animal kingdom?

5. Read another book about Africa, possibly *The Flame Trees of Thika*, by Elspeth Huxley, or *West with the Night*, by Beryl Markham, and compare one of these with *Born Free*, by Joy Adamson. Which woman wrote the best book? Why do you think so? Explain.

13. Born Free

Answers

True or False and Why?

1. +
2. 0; chasing elephants
3. 0; It was a total failure, embarrassing.
4. +
5. 0; She first learned to kill a wild pig.
6. +
7. +
8. 0; George and Joy stayed together through the whole ordeal.
9. 0; Elsa returned regularly to visit with the Adamsons and to show her cubs to Joy.
10. 0; Joy learned her lesson and never took in another large, wild animal to tame.

Short Answers

1. Joy had a schoolmate whose name was Elsa.
2. He knows she is wild at heart.
3. Elsa chased a herd of elephants through a village, and caused much damage.
4. to kill other animals for food; to protect herself from being killed
5. They wanted to be where they could be themselves, away from noise and social pressure.
6. She was too large for the house; she scared visitors; she had to be protected from wild creatures.
7. Joy had no children of her own; she loved animals.
8. Answers will vary.
9. Answers will vary.
10. Answers will vary

Vocabulary

(1) menace—a threat   (2) province—a territory   (3) safari—an expedition (usually for hunting)   (4) formula—liquid infant food   (5) pride—a group of lions   (6) reserve—an area of land set aside for a specific purpose   (7) rendezvous—a prearranged meeting
(8) precedent—an example   (9) emancipation—the act of granting freedom
(10) ecstatic—overjoyed

Sample essay:

> On a game *reserve* in East Africa, George Adamson shoots a female lion and takes her three cubs home. His wife, Joy, feeds the cubs a special *formula* and is *ecstatic* when the cubs respond to it. But soon the cubs become a *menace* around the Adamson home, and Joy and George decide to give them to a zoo. George, however, keeps the smallest lion cub, Elsa, for Joy to raise as a pet. It becomes obvious that Elsa needs *emancipation* from the tame life at home, and Joy tries to release her. But Elsa is tame and can't compete in a normal *pride*, so George and Joy eventually train her to live on her own and set Elsa off in the wild to make it or die as a free lion.

Essay Topics

Essays will vary.

14. WHEN THE LEGENDS DIE

Author: Hal Borland
Novel Title: *When the Legends Die*
Director: Stuart Miller

Running Time: 105 minutes
Year: 1972
Format: color

Summary

Tom Blackbull is a Ute Indian boy who lives alone in the mountains after his parents have died. He lives in "the old way," singing songs and prayers at morning and at night. He is content to be alone with a bear he calls "my brother."

One day, Tom is visited by Blue Elk, an old Indian man who talks Tom into coming down off the mountain to attend a reservation school. Tom brings his bear with him, but soon learns that the school wants to take his old life away and give him "new ways." The bear is chained to a post and Tom is locked in a room alone after fighting with one of the boys. The following day, Blue Elk ties Tom's hands like a criminal and leads him and the bear back up the mountain, where Blue Elk forces Tom to scare the bear off and to come back down into civilization.

Years pass and we see Tom as a young man herding horses for the reservation school. He rides and breaks them when he can, but is caught by the foreman and is demoted to herding sheep. He is refused all contact with the horses, the only things he truly loves and respects.

While Tom is crossing the street in town one afternoon, a cowboy sets him up to ride a vicious horse for the price of one dollar. Tom breaks the horse, takes the dollar, and walks away. But he doesn't get far when a crusty old bronc rider/ gambler named Red asks Tom if he wants to make some real money. Tom says yes, and Red takes him on as a partner, signing custody papers to be the guardian of "a real Ute Indian."

Red teaches Tom to "throw" rodeo events— intentionally losing the first round—so the bets against Tom will increase in the second half of the rodeo. This way, Red wins ten times the money and can get ten times as drunk.

Tom eventually begins to feel like a thief, and he tells Red that he wants to ride to win, honestly and fairly. "I'm good. I can do it!" Tom says.

But Red will have none of it and beats Tom unconscious, then dumps him into the back of the pickup and drives off to the next rodeo.

Tom becomes bitter, and takes it out on the horses he rides. He kills several horses by riding them to death, thus earning the rodeo name Killer Tom Black. Tom continues to ride this way till his anger clears enough for him to see that Red is nothing without him, and he leaves Red at a gas station, tosses Red's saddle over a bridge, and drives off to build a life for himself.

Months later at a small-town rodeo, a horse goes over backward, crushing Tom beneath it. Tom recuperates for several months at the home of a young nurse he has met in the hospital. She wants a permanent relationship, but Tom is restless. One morning he writes her a note, and then leaves.

He ends up at Red's shack, bearing the gift of a new saddle. He find Red living alone—Mayo, Red's former partner and cook, is dead. Tom wants to rebuild some kind of relationship with Red, but Red is arrogant. He wants what he used to have—money and fame from Tom's skill on the rodeo circuit.

That night, Red takes Tom's car and drives to town, where he drinks himself into a collapse. Red dies in the hospital, and Tom leaves for the reservation. He asks for the superintendent, but ends up meeting with a board of control made up of Indian men. Tom says he has learned the "new ways," now he wants to teach the younger ones the "old ways." The movie ends when Tom says, "I want to be with the horses." Tom's healing and growth depend on his relationship with nature, with the animals he knows best. In the white man's world he has found only pain and broken dreams. With the horses, he has a chance to find a full and meaningful life.

Name _____   Date _____

14. When the Legends Die

Fill in the Blank

After watching the movie *When the Legends Die*, fill in the blanks in the summary below with the correct information.

An Indian boy named (1) _____ finds himself living alone in the mountains with a (2) _____ as his only companion. He lives in "the old way" as the modern Indians call it, which means he lives off the land, away from people, in a (3) _____.

The boy is taken to a reservation school by an old man named (4) _____ _____. There the boy is given a room, some clothes, and an education. He resists, but to no avail. He stays at the school in a dorm room until he is almost an adult.

One day a cowboy offers Tom a (5) _____ to ride an unbroken horse, and Tom rides until the horse stops bucking. Tom takes the (6) _____ from the cowboy and starts to walk off when a man named (7) _____ stops him and says, "Why don't you ride for me, kid. We can get rich and live forever!"

Tom becomes a saddle bronc rider and travels all over the country winning money at several (8) _____. But there's a catch. He must lose the first round or two in order to look bad. Then his partner, old Red, bets a lot of money on Tom, and people who think the Indian is a loser bet a lot of their money against Tom. Then Tom wins the final ride, and he and Red take all the money.

Tom hates this arrangement because he knows he could be a real (9) _____. Tom (10) _____ Red, and goes out on his own. He wins championship after championship, and at one point tells Red, "Last year I won (11) _____ dollars."

Red is a bitter old con man who spends all his money on (12) _____. One day Red has too much and (13) _____. Tom is then alone in the world and has only a life of bronc-riding and broken bones ahead of him. He goes back to the reservation school and asks for the superintendent. "I have learned the (14) _____ _____," Tom said. "I want to be with the (15) _____."

And so the story ends as it began—Tom, a (16) _____ Indian, gets separated from all he knows, then struggles in the white man's world, succeeds, but returns to his native land to help his people. He has learned that when the legends die, it is time to start over and make new ones with the life you have left.

---

14. When the Legends Die

Indian Songs

When Tom lived in "the old way" he spent days in the mountains hunting, killing, and cooking his own food. He gathered wood for his fire, hauled water from the river, and spread elk robes and deer hides on the tepee floor to keep out the cold. In the tradition of Native Americans, Tom sang songs for each of these activities. He had a rising song to greet the morning, a hunting song to help him find the deer, and a celebration song for when the deer was killed.

These songs were meant to strengthen Tom's spirit and to give him communication with the Great Spirit who made the earth and all the things on the earth. A celebration song after a hunt might go like this:

> I have killed the deer.
> With my bow and strong arrows
> I have killed him.
> There is thunder in my bow.
> There is thunder in me.
> I have killed the deer.
> I will take his heart home.

Try to imagine yourself in Tom's place. You are alone. Your parents are dead. You must wake each day and face the world on your own. What will be the morning song that you sing to the rising sun? Or what will your evening song be, when you sing to the setting sun? On the lines below, write your song. Use short lines. Repeat a key phrase as in the example above.

_____

_____

_____

_____

_____

_____

_____

14. When the Legends Die

Character Analysis

If you watched *When the Legends Die* carefully, you probably came away with a feeling that you knew the main characters very well—Red Dillon, the selfish, hard-drinking rodeo gambler, and Tom Blackbull, the hard-riding Indian boy who was taken in by Red in more ways than one.

Below are listed several concepts that are central to the action of the movie. Think about how each concept was viewed differently by the two main characters. Describe Red's and Tom's views on each concept.

RED DILLON	TOM BLACKBULL
Horses _____ _____ _____	Horses _____ _____ _____
Honesty _____ _____ _____	Honesty _____ _____ _____
Friendship _____ _____ _____	Friendship _____ _____ _____
Money _____ _____ _____	Money _____ _____ _____
Fame _____ _____ _____	Fame _____ _____ _____
The Future _____ _____ _____	The Future _____ _____ _____
"The Old Ways" _____ _____ _____	"The Old Ways" _____ _____ _____

14. When the Legends Die

Prepositions and Prepositional Phrases

Without prepositions, you would have to say things like: "I'm going the store"; or "We'll be home three o'clock." Prepositions give rhythm to our language and help us connect ideas as expressed in words. But prepositions don't act alone; they are always tied to a noun:

to the *store*   by *three o'clock*
before the next *train*   beside still *waters*

Below are two paragraphs about the movie *When the Legends Die*. Write in the prepositions on the lines provided to help the sentences make sense. Sometimes a blank could be filled with one of several prepositions, depending on what you interpret the sentence to mean. There is a list of prepositions below the paragraphs (you may use the same preposition more than once). After writing in the prepositions, circle each prepositional phrase.

Example: Tom Blackbull went everywhere <u>*in*</u> an old GMC truck.

(1) _____ the mountains, (2) _____ modern conveniences or any help

(3) _____ adults, young Tom Blackbull lived (4) ____ a tepee (5) _____

a wild bear he had tamed. He could roam where he wished, sleep when he got

tired, and eat all the fish he could catch. But modern society caught up

(6) _____ him and pulled him down (7) ____ the city and (8) _____the

white man's ways.

(9) ____ the reservation school where society eventually placed Tom, he

worked (10) _____ the wild mustangs and broke them (11) ____ riding.

He spent his days (12) ____ the sun and wind doing what he liked best. But

fame and fortune soon found him and he became ensnared (13) _____ a

world (14) ____ gamblers, crooks, and drunks who thought (15) _____

horses as "meat," something to be purchased and consumed.

Prepositions

aboard, about, above, across, after, against, along, amid, among, around, at, before behind, below, beneath, beside, between, beyond, but (except), by, down, during, except for, from, in, into, like, near, of, off, on, over, past since, through, throughout, to toward, under, underneath, until, unto, up, upon, with, within, without

14. When the Legends Die

Answers

Fill in the Blank

(1) Tom (Blackbull)
(2) bear
(3) tepee
(4) Blue Elk
(5) dollar
(6) dollar (money)
(7) Red (Dillon)
(8) rodeos

(9) champion
(10) leaves (abandons)
(11) $17,000
(12) whiskey (alcohol)
(13) dies
(14) new ways
(15) horses
(16) Ute

Indian Songs

Poems will vary.

Character Analysis

Red Dillon:

Horses—These were simply gambling devices from which Red made drinking money.
Honesty—Red lied and cheated to get what he wanted.
Friendship—Red's "friends" were people from whom he could get something.
Money—Red used money to get whiskey and to prove he was more clever than others.
Fame—Red had no concept of fame. He wanted to hide so he could cheat people more easily.
The Future—Red lived day by day, bottle to bottle.
"The Old Ways"—Red had no feeling for the past, for traditions.

Tom Blackbull:

Horses—Horses were Tom's soul mates, and a link to his Indian past. He respected horses.
Honesty—Tom felt that being honest was the only way to live a truly free life.
Friendship—Tom's friends were the horses. He wanted to be friends with Red, but Red wanted only to be the scheming boss and have a "business" relationship.
Money—Tom wanted to be skilled rather than be rich. He saw money as the white man's way of controlling and using people.
Fame—Tom wanted to be known for being a great rider and horseman.
The Future—Tom wanted a purpose in life; that's why he went back to the reservation to work with the horses and possibly teach others to ride.
"The Old Ways"—Tom believed that the old ways were best, that modern ways were brutal and dishonest.

Prepositions

Some answers will vary.
(1) in (2) without (3) from (4) in (5) with (6) to/with (7) to/into (8) to/toward/into (9) at (10) with/amid (11) by/through (12) in (13) by/in (14) of (15) of/about

15. FAHRENHEIT 451

Author: Ray Bradbury
Novel Title: *Fahrenheit 451*
Director: François Truffaut

Running Time: 112 minutes
Year: 1966
Format: color

Summary

A team of firemen dressed in black and riding a fire truck race to the home of a person who owns books. A little boy watching the action says to his mother, "Look, Mommy! There's going to be a fire!" The firemen confiscate all the books they find in the home, pile them on the sidewalk, and set them ablaze with a flamethrower. This is how the movie *Fahrenheit 451* begins and ends, with books as the subject of interest.

In *Fahrenheit 451* society, books are illegal. People who own them or even read them are imprisoned. The protagonist in the film, Montag, is a middle-aged fireman who is about to be promoted for his allegiance to his job and to his commander. But he meets a young girl, whose name is never given, and the beginning of the end of his career is set in motion.

Montag's marriage is disintegrating because his wife is so addicted to the telescreen that she's losing her personality. She watches infantile game shows in which the host turns to the viewers, calls their names, and waits for those called upon to phone in an answer or suggestion. This "interaction" is what *Fahrenheit 451* society tries to promote, using everything from stimulants to violence to achieve its aim.

One day Montag comes home from work to find his wife unconscious from an overdose of the government's stimulant. He calls the medical people, who pump out Linda's old blood and put in new. These impromptu transfusions are commonplace, and Montag is not to worry. That night Montag stays up late to read a book—his first.

The next day, on the way to work, the unnamed girl "accidentally" bumps into Montag and she's crying. She tells him she's been fired. He agrees to go to the school where she teaches and talk for her. The girl calls in "sick" for Montag, then the two travel to the school where she is shunned by the children for being unique—for being a book person. That night Montag confesses to his wife that he reads books and she insists that either the books go, or she goes. The next morning at the fire station Montag reaches for the firepole, but it will not pull him up to his work station; he has lost spiritual contact with *Fahrenheit* society.

On that day's assignment the young girl's house is plundered by the firemen, but the firemen never get the chance to burn the books. Before Montag's eyes, a woman, the young girl's friend, lights herself on fire, consuming the books and herself in the flames. Montag is never the same after this. He breaks into the captain's office the following day looking for information about the girl, is discovered, and finds that she has not been arrested but is under investigation.

Montag's wife, Linda, leaves him and drops his photo into one of the red information boxes which stand at every street corner in the city. She has betrayed him as a reader of books, and now the scene is set for the climax.

The captain asks Montag to accompany him to a book-burning at Montag's house. Montag is handed the flamethrower, whereupon he burns his wife's bed, and then turns the flamethrower on the captain, who falls onto a pile of burning books and is consumed in flames. Montag runs to the woods, where the book people live, and there finds the girl and hundreds of other people who have taken titles of famous books for their personal names. These people become books and spend their days chanting their contents so as not to let the ideas die in the flames of the firemen's torches, which ignite to the temperature of burning paper: 451 degrees Fahrenheit.

15. Fahrenheit 451

Multiple Choice

Circle the letter of the correct answer to each question below.

1. Montag's job title is: (a) secret police (b) book burner (c) fireman (d) librarian

2. In his daily work, Montag: (a) arrests book sellers (b) burns encyclopedias and dictionaries (c) burns all books he can find (d) interrogates prisoners

3. The movie opens with (a) the police burning a man at the stake (b) a book raid by the firemen (c) a firemen's picnic (d) a firemen's rally (e) both a and b

4. Which reason for avoiding books does Montag *not* give to the girl: (a) it is illegal (b) he's not interested (c) it's too expensive (d) Montag has better things to do

5. What is the government's stated main purpose, or goal? (a) to burn all books (b) to keep people afraid of the police (c) to keep people equal and "happy" (d) to find and prosecute criminals

6. What is a "wall screen"? (a) a painting (b) a living mural (c) a living photograph (d) a huge television screen (e) none of the above

7. What does the wall screen do? (a) controls people's minds (b) gives people something to do besides read (c) makes people feel like they belong to a family (d) spies on people who hide books (e) both a and b (f) both a and d (g) all but d (h) none of the above

8. The captain thinks people should stay active in sports because: (a) it keeps citizens busy and happy (b) sports keep people away from books (c) sports give the firemen extra income (d) both a and c (e) both a and b (f) all of the above (g) none of the above

9. The person who betrayed Montag was: (a) Fabian (b) the captain (c) his wife (d) a friend

10. In order to escape, Montag burns: (a) his wife (b) his wife's bed (c) the wall screen (d) the captain (e) Fabian (f) a, b, and c (g) a, d, and e (h) none of the above

15. Fahrenheit 451

Short Answers

On the lines provided beneath each quotation, tell what the quote means; explain in your own words what it has to say about the people and the quality of life in *Fahrenheit 451* society.

1. The voice on the wall screen says, "Come play with us, cousins!"

   _____

   _____

2. Linda says, "They say [owning] another wall screen makes you feel your family has grown out around you."

   _____

   _____

3. Montag says, "Behind each of these books is a man!"

   _____

   _____

4. A little boy says, "Look, Mommy! There's going to be a fire!"

   _____

   _____

5. The captain says, "The books have nothing to say!"

   _____

   _____

6. Montag says, "You are not living. You are all killing time!"

   _____

   _____

7. The girl says, "The people *are* the books!"

   _____

   _____

8. The book people leader says, "Come and watch your [Montag's] capture on the screen."

   _____

   _____

15. Fahrenheit 451

Terms to Understand

The words, concepts, and phrases listed below are used exclusively in the strange society of *Fahrenheit 451*. Read each term or phrase and then draw a line to the definition or explanation of that term or phrase.

1. Fahrenheit 451

   a pill that keeps you alert

2. blood transfusion

   a book of fiction

3. information box

   a mindless, empty person

4. zombie

   a person who loves fire

5. pyromaniac

   an oppressive, book-burning society; the temperature at which paper burns

6. novel

   replaces drug-overdosed blood with fresh supply

7. stimulant

   a photo receptacle on the street corner

   a person who has books

8. book people

   book-lovers who memorize a book, then burn it

9. kerosene

   the state of being without emotion; drugged

10. fireman

    a person who burns books on command

11. wall screen

    the "perfume" of the firemen

12. happiness

    a huge, mind-controlling television

13. criminal

    to say the words in a book aloud from memory

14. rocking chair

    where people used to sit and visit before the wall screen took over

15. to "recite oneself"

15. Fahrenheit 451

Compound Sentences

A compound sentence is one that is made of two or more separate sentences (called "independent clauses") joined by a conjunction such as *yet, or, for, but, and.*

Example:　　The firemen ransacked people's houses,
for they knew there were books hidden inside.

The first sentence "The firemen ransacked people's houses" and the second sentence "they knew there were books hidden inside" are joined by the word "for," which is a conjunction.

Make each pair of independent clauses below into one compound sentence by using one of the conjunctions listed above.

1. Firemen piled the books on the front lawn.
   They burned them with a flamethrower.

   _____

2. The woman burned herself and her books.
   She didn't want to risk being interrogated.

   _____

3. Montag was about to get a promotion.
   His captain didn't know that Montag was reading books.

   _____

4. Montag knew of the risks involved.
   He let the young teacher lie for him about being sick.

   _____

5. Montag grabbed onto the pole.
   It would not take him upstairs.

   _____

6. Most firemen put out fires.
   These start fires.

   _____

7. In Montag's world, people can avoid reading books.
   They can go to jail.

   _____

15. Fahrenheit 451

Answers

Multiple Choice
(1) c   (2) c   (3) b   (4) c   (5) c   (6) d   (7) g   (8) e   (9) c   (10) d

Short Answers

1. The announcer is asking the viewers to come participate in the program. Society treats its citizens like children who have no friends or family and need guidance.
2. The wall screen is society's family: people talk to it and interact with it. Another wall screen brings more contact with game show hosts.
3. The books are individual ideas from real people's minds, something illegal in the strange society of *Fahrenheit 451.*
4. The firemen in *451* society start fires rather than put them out. They find books and burn them so people can't get any independent ideas.
5. The society, exemplified by the captain, believes that books and ideas breed confusion and unrest; people ask questions of politicians, teachers, and preachers, and that is not allowed.
6. Montag believes that to be fully alive one must think lively thoughts, original thoughts. The people of *451* society simply absorb nonsense from the game shows on the wall screen.
7. The book people memorize their favorite book, then burn it. They recite the book word for word, and the book becomes the only life they have.
8. *451* society makes media events out of everything to keep people watching. Here, *451* police have killed an innocent man, rather than Montag, just to have something to show on the wall screen.

Terms to Understand

1. Fahrenheit 451—an oppressive, book-burning society; the temperature at which paper burns
2. blood transfusion—replaces drug-overdosed blood with fresh supply
3. information box—a photo receptacle on the street corner
4. zombie—a mindless, empty person
5. pyromaniac—a person who loves fire
6. novel—a book of fiction
7. stimulant—a pill that keeps you alert
8. book people—book-lovers who memorize a book, then burn it
9. kerosene—the "perfume" of the firemen
10. fireman—a person who burns books on command
11. wall screen—a huge, mind-controlling television
12. happiness—the state of being without emotion; drugged
13. criminal—a person who has books
14. rocking chair—where people used to sit and visit before the wall screen took over
15. to "recite oneself"—to say the words in a book aloud from memory

Compound Sentences

Answers may vary.   (1) and   (2) for   (3) but   (4) yet   (5) yet   (6) but   (7) or

16. OLIVER!

Author: Charles Dickens
Novel Title: *Oliver Twist*
Director: Carol Reed

Running Time: 153 minutes
Year: 1968
Format: color

Summary

Oliver! is the musical version of Charles Dickens's classic story of the orphan Oliver Twist, who struggles for survival in the slums of London. It starts with a boy who has no mother, no name, no home, no friends, and who's been scooped up by the system and dumped into a workhouse run by a Mr. Bumble. Bumble is fat, mean, and small-minded. He names Oliver, but forgets about the boy until the day Oliver walks to the front of the mess hall and asks for "more."

"More?!" screams Bumble. And Oliver's adventure begins.

He is sold to Mr. Sourberry, the town mortician, who wants Oliver for his "melancholy look"; the boy will march in funeral processions to earn his keep. But Sourberry's apprentice insults the name of Oliver's dead mother and Oliver responds with a hammer. Bumble is called and Oliver is thrown into the cellar. "He's mad!" cries Mrs. Sourberry. "It's not madness, ma'am. It's meat. You've overfed him!" says the waddling Bumble.

Oliver runs away to London, where he meets Jack Dawkins, the "Artful Dodger." The Dodger brings him to Fagin, a greasy old character who keeps a stable of pickpockets in his "lodgings." Fagin calls them "dears" and feeds them sausages. Oliver naively accepts the invitation to "work" like the other boys and become as accomplished as the Dodger at the art of collecting scarves and wallets from London's elite.

On his first "job," Oliver is left standing next to a Mr. Brownlow, who has just been robbed by the Dodger. Brownlow says, "Give it back, boy," while staring at Oliver. Oliver runs, is caught, and is dragged before the magistrate. A bookseller testifies that Oliver was not the boy who stole Brownlow's wallet, and Oliver is free. Brownlow takes Oliver home and notices a shocking resemblance between the boy and the photograph of Brownlow's niece, Emily.

On an errand for Brownlow, Oliver is kidnapped by two of Fagin's accomplices, Bill Sykes and his girlfriend Nancy. Oliver is brought back to the lodgings. Bill plans a heist using Oliver as the break-in man, but Nancy resists. She does not want Oliver used as she had been as a child. "Tonight he [Oliver] becomes a thief and a liar," Bill says, and stalks out of the room.

Meanwhile Brownlow has placed ads seeking information about Oliver's identity, and Bumble and his conniving wife have shown up with Oliver's mother's locket. Brownlow now knows that the boy is part of his family, and does everything he can to recover him. Nancy goes to see Brownlow, in response to his ad, to set up Oliver's escape. She will bring the boy to London Bridge at midnight. Brownlow is to be there alone.

Bill Sykes sees Nancy leaving the tavern with Oliver and follows. In a fit of anger, he kills Nancy at the bridge and runs to Fagin's with the boy in tow. Fagin is appalled at Bill's stupidity and scatters for parts unknown. Meanwhile, Bill's dog, Bullseye, has led the police to Fagin's place. In a dramatic scene in which Bill and Oliver are on a fire escape, Bill is shot and swings from a rope high above the crowd that has gathered for the chase.

In the final scene, Fagin and the Dodger meet in a back alley. Fagin has lost his treasure box in the open sewer ditch that runs past his lodgings, and the Dodger has "lifted" a fine specimen of a wallet from a man who was watching Bill Sykes's corpse swing in midair. Fagin, who has just determined to go forth into the world and get a legitimate job, "reviews the situation," links arms with the Dodger, and they skip their way out of London to prove that crime does pay.

Oliver is last seen entering the home of Mr. Brownlow, who will now give the boy his proper identity and a much better life.

16. Oliver!

Multiple Choice

Write the letter of the correct answer for each item on the line provided.

1. ____ In the opening scene of the movie the boys are: (a) eating (b) singing (c) reciting the workhouse code (d) working

2. ____ Oliver's troubles begin when he: (a) plans to run away from Mr. Bumble (b) snitches on his friends (c) asks for more gruel (d) smacks Mr. Bumble on the nose

3. ____ Oliver is sold to the undertaker, Mr. Sourberry, because: (a) Oliver was ungrateful (b) Oliver was cruel (c) Oliver was depressed (d) Oliver was overfed

4. ____ At Sourberry's, Oliver attacks Noah Claypole, the apprentice, because: (a) Claypole lied about Oliver (b) Claypole was picking on him (c) Claypole was meddling in Oliver's personal affairs (d) Claypole said nasty things about Oliver's mother

5. ____ What Oliver wants most in the world is: (a) to be loved (b) to be rich and free (c) to be an adult (d) to have a best friend (e) to have a fine career

6. ____ In London, after Oliver runs away from Sourberry, he meets Jack Dawkins, who is called: (a) the "Creeper" (b) the "Artful Dodger" (c) the "Merry Munchkin" (d) the "Little Thief"

7. ____ Oliver teams up with Fagin and the boys because: (a) Oliver wants to feel a part of a family (b) he wants food and shelter (c) he needs to make a living (d) he wants to learn to become a doctor like Fagin (e) both a and b (f) a, b, and c (g) a, b, c, and d (h) none of the above

8. ____ In the song "Consider Yourself One of Us," the word *us* refers to: (a) the gang (b) Fagin and Bill Sykes (c) the poor class of London (d) the criminals of London

9. ____ Fagin makes his living by: (a) stealing (b) selling stolen goods (c) laundering handkerchiefs (d) renting rooms to thieves and other criminals (e) running a tavern

10. ____ Bill Sykes is clearly the _____ in the story. (a) hero (b) victim (c) villain

16. Oliver!

Vocabulary

Look up the words listed in the box below, using a dictionary. Once you know what each word means, use all fifteen words in the fifteen sentences by writing them on the lines provided.

paupers
purloin
magistrate
nocturnal
orphan
melancholy
farthing
pact
niece
heinous
incorrigible
collusion
proficient
corpulent
ingrate

1. The sign on the workhouse gate said that _____ and orphans lived there.

2. Fagin taught the boys to _____ items from people's pockets.

3. The boys had hopes of becoming as _____ at stealing as Bill Sykes had become.

4. Bill Sykes committed a _____ crime when he killed Nancy.

5. When Oliver first gets to London he's poor; he hasn't got a _____.

6. Nancy and Bill worked in _____ to kidnap Oliver and bring him to Fagin.

7. The boys in the workhouse were skinny, while the adults were _____.

8. When Oliver asked for more gruel he was called an _____.

9. Mr. Brownlow rescued Oliver after the boy was brought before the _____.

10. Fagin's personal business was never conducted in daylight; he was a _____ crook.

11. Mr. Brownlow realized that Oliver looked a lot like his _____.

12. Oliver's greatest sadness was that he was an _____.

13. Oliver was hired by the undertaker because of the look of _____ on the boy's face.

14. At the end, the Dodger proves that he is an _____ pickpocket.

15. Fagin has made an unwritten _____ with his boys—they steal, while he feeds and clothes them and gives them a place to "belong."

16. Oliver!

Character Analysis

Choose eight of the characters listed below to fit into the following categories: "good," "bad," and "both good and bad." Then write their names on the blanks in the proper columns and tell what each character *did* and *said* that caused you to see him or her as good, bad, or a mixture of both.

Oliver   Artful Dodger   Fagin   Nancy   Mr. Sourberry   Mr. Bumble   Bill Sykes

Mrs. Bumble   Mr. Brownlow   Mrs. Sourberry   Brownlow's maid   the bookseller

GOOD	GOOD & BAD	BAD
#1 _____	#4 _____	#6 _____
#2 _____		#7 _____
#3 _____	#5 _____	#8 _____

Name _____ Date _____

16. Oliver!

Projects

Below is a list of projects based on the movie *Oliver!* Choose one that suits your interests and abilities, then check with your teacher about such things as due date, available materials, and working with a classmate. *Note*: Remember that many resources exist outside the school building, particularly people who have skills, ideas, and materials that they would be happy to share with you, if you only ask.

1. The movie *Oliver!* is filled with music, dance, and good song lyrics. Choose a song from the film, either a solo, such as Oliver's "Where Is Love?" or Nancy's song about her love for Bill Sykes. Learn the song and sing it for the class. Or you might videotape yourself at home and show the tape to your classmates. If you'd rather not do a song from the movie, write your own—possibly something about the Artful Dodger, or about Oliver's mother. Then perform it for the class.

2. If you enjoy building things, you could create a model of Fagin's hideout using a simple cardboard box as the "room," then adding pieces made from wood, sugar cubes, toothpicks, or cardboard (cereal boxes). You could include a battery-powered light in one corner of the box to provide atmosphere. If you're really daring, you may wish to get a piece of plywood and build a model of the entire street outside Fagin's hideout. You will probably want to use papier-mâché and some sort of screen or wire to provide the foundation for all the pieces needed to make the scene.

3. Make a tombstone for Oliver's mother, Emily Brownlow, and write a brief, moving **epitaph** on the stone, telling something about her character. Then make up a short, one-page **eulogy** that you may read to the class as if you were standing at Emily's grave on the day of her burial.

4. Fagin is a criminal of the friendly sort; he doesn't want to hurt anyone, just relieve them of some of their personal belongings. A court of law would definitely try to convict him, but on what charges—theft, possession of stolen property, contributing to the delinquency of minors (children)? Prepare a court case that includes *both* sides of the issue of Fagin's guilt. You must be the defense lawyer who is trying to prove Fagin innocent, and then you must take on the role of prosecuting attorney in trying to get Fagin sent to jail. Maybe a classmate will work with you on this, and you can argue your case before the "court" (with the teacher and students as judge and jury) using yet another classmate to play the role of Fagin, the lovable thief.

5. Make a "wanted" poster for the villain, Bill Sykes, listing his assumed names, his crimes, the price on his head, and what legal authority to contact. Then write a short biography of Bill Sykes that tells of his childhood and youth in the slums of London, and read it to the class. If you can't sketch his face, maybe a classmate will help you. Or you could make a photocopy of a photograph that you've "touched up."

6. Sara Teasdale wrote a poem called "Faults." Memorize the poem and say it to your classmates or put it to music and sing it to them. Or write out a poster-size copy of the poem in the artful handwriting called **calligraphy**. You could also discuss the poem as it might apply to Nancy in *Oliver!*

16. Oliver!

Answers

Multiple Choice

(1) d   (2) c   (3) a   (4) d   (5) a   (6) b   (7) f   (8) c   (9) b   (10) c

Vocabulary

(1) paupers	(6) collusion	(11) niece
(2) purloin	(7) corpulent	(12) orphan
(3) proficient	(8) ingrate	(13) melancholy
(4) heinous	(9) magistrate	(14) incorrigible
(5) farthing	(10) nocturnal	(15) pact

Character Analysis

Good—Oliver, Brownlow, the bookseller (or) Brownlow's maid

Good and Bad—Fagin, Nancy (or) Artful Dodger

Bad—Bill Sykes, Mr. Bumble, Mrs. Bumble (or) Mr. Sourberry (or) Mrs. Sourberry

(Explanations will vary.)

Projects

Projects will vary.

17. WEST SIDE STORY

Author: Arthur Laurents
Play Title: *West Side Story*
Director: Robert Wise

Running Time: 151 minutes
Year: 1961
Format: color

Summary

After an opening "rumble" between the Jets (the whites) and the Sharks (Puerto Ricans), Riff, the Jets' leader, goes to Tony, his best friend and cofounder of the gang, and asks him to come to the dance that night to help organize a "war council" with the Sharks. Tony agrees to go, but not before telling Riff of a dream he's had lately where he wakes up in the night reaching out for something. At the dance that night, Tony's dream is realized when he sees Maria, a beautiful Puerto Rican girl who is the sister of Bernardo, the Sharks' leader. Bernardo sends Maria home with Chino, Bernardo's "best man," and then stays to form a war council with the Jets.

At Doc's that night, Tony steps in and suggests that the best man from each gang "slug it out" in a fair fight. The gangs agree. When the store is empty, Tony tells Doc about Maria. Doc says, "I'm afraid enough for both of you." Tony goes to Maria's place and is discovered by Anita, Bernardo's girl. Anita promises not to tell on them, then leaves. Maria makes Tony promise to stop *any* fighting. Tony agrees.

When Tony arrives at the rumble, Ice (the Jets' "best man") and Bernardo are fist-fighting. Tony steps in to stop the fight but is pushed and teased by Bernardo to the point that Riff jumps in with a knife. Bernardo stabs Riff; then in a fury Tony grabs Riff's knife and kills Bernardo.

Chino runs to Maria with the terrible news and is enraged when Maria asks first about Tony rather than about her brother Bernardo. Chino runs out and Tony arrives. "I didn't know it was going to happen. I didn't want it to happen," he says. They kiss, and plan to run away to where no one can get to them.

Meanwhile the Jets meet to form a strategy: be cool, don't let any emotions show. The impish female character called "Anybody's" tells the gang that she overheard Chino say he's going to kill Tony. The Jets scatter to find Tony before Chino does.

Anita comes home to find Tony leaving via the window. She warns Maria about the danger of loving a white boy, but Maria convinces Anita of the quality of her and Tony's love. Lieutenant Shrank shows up at Maria's apartment to question her, and Anita agrees to go to Doc's for "aspirin" and to leave the message that Maria has been "detained." Anita is met at Doc's by the Jets, who believe she has come on Chino's behalf. They become violent and are about to rape her when Doc walks in. He scorns them, and Anita frees herself and heads for the door. But before she goes she tells them to give a message to their "American buddy"—"Maria is dead! Chino found out about them and shot her!"

Doc tells Tony, who goes crazy with grief and runs through the streets shouting Chino's name. He wants to die. He wants Chino to shoot him and end his pain. But then he sees Maria coming toward him, calling his name. He runs to her and is gunned down by Chino.

The gangs gather around the figure of Maria holding Tony in her arms. She takes Chino's pistol, waves it at the Jets, then at the Sharks, and says, "You all killed them, Riff, my brother, and Tony—you killed them with hate! Now I can kill too, because now I have hate!" The film ends with the Puerto Ricans helping the Jets carry Tony's body from the playground, which was the scene of the first "rumble" of the film. Baby John, a young Jet gang member, places a black shawl over Maria's head. Then the crowd disperses.

17. West Side Story

Multiple Choice

Circle the letter of the correct answer for each of the items below.

1. The major conflict in the film is between which two groups? (a) blacks and whites (b) Mexicans and whites (c) Asians and Puerto Ricans (d) Puerto Ricans and whites

2. The conflict between the Sharks and the Jets is over: (a) revenge (b) spying (c) turf (d) racial hate (e) both a and b (f) both c and d (g) none of the above

3. Who is killed in the movie *West Side Story*? (a) Anita (b) Anita, Tony, and Riff (c) Anita, Tony, Riff, and Bernardo (d) Tony, Riff, and Bernardo

4. Tony is advised not to fall in love with Maria because: (a) she's Puerto Rican (b) she is a spy for the Sharks (c) she will betray him (d) she pushes drugs

5. How is Tony connected to the Jets? (a) he supplies them with war plans (b) he is Riff's stepbrother (c) he founded the gang with Riff (d) he used to be their leader (e) both c and d

6. What is Doc's relationship with the gangs? (a) he gives them a place to gather (b) he gives them advice (c) he is their informer (d) he helps decide war councils (e) both a and b

7. Why don't the Puerto Ricans want to go back to Puerto Rico? (a) they are afraid of being hated by their people (b) they have more opportunity here (c) they can be more free here in America (d) in Puerto Rico they have less than they have in America (e) b, c, and d (f) a, b, and d

8. The lieutenant tells the Jets that he's on their side, but in reality: (a) he's a Puerto Rican at heart (b) he wants the streets cleared of all "punks" (c) he doesn't care what they do

9. When Ice says, "Be cool!" he means: (a) don't let your feelings show (b) avoid the cops (c) take a cold shower (d) wear the "right" clothes (e) dance like a pro

10. Why does Anita lie about Maria being killed? (a) she wants revenge for Bernardo (b) she hopes Tony will try to take revenge on Chino and get killed (c) she was mistreated by the whites and hates them (d) all of the above (e) both a and b (f) both a and c

Name _____ Date _____

17. West Side Story

Pronouns/Verb Agreement

When pronouns like *each*, *both*, and *some* are subjects of sentences, it's sometimes difficult to know what verb form to use. But the rule for proper sentence-building still holds—a singular subject requires a singular verb, and a plural subject requires a plural verb. Below are three groups of pronouns. Group #1 requires singular verbs; group #2 requires plural verbs; and group #3 uses either a singular or a plural verb depending on the context of the sentence.

Examples: Each of the boys *was* confused.   (singular)
Both of the boys *were* confused.   (plural)
Some of the pizza *was* moldy.   (dual: singular)
Some of the pizzas *were* moldy.   (dual: plural)

Group #1 (singular): one, each, either, neither, somebody, nobody, anybody, everybody, no one, someone, anyone, everyone, nothing, something, anything, everything, much, another

Group #2 (plural): many, few, several, both, others

Group #3 (singular or plural): some, none, all, most, any

Circle the correct form of the verb in each sentence:

1. Each of the gang members (were, was) afraid.

2. None of them (want, wants) to die.

3. Everyone (sings, sing) in *West Side Story.*

4. Both Maria and Tony (loves, love) each other.

5. Some of the gang members on both sides (thinks, think) Tony is a coward.

6. Everybody in the Jets (look, looks) up to Tony.

7. No one in the Sharks (argues, argue) with Bernardo.

8. Nobody (seems, seem) to have the answer for these ghetto kids.

9. All of their futures (is, are) at stake.

10. Neither Tony nor Maria (believe, believes) violence is the answer.

11. Each of the gangs' leaders (was, were) killed at the rumble.

12. Neither of the leaders (was, were) ready to die.

17. West Side Story

Oral Communication

We speak more often than we write, but not formally. Below is an exercise in public speaking that requires good poise, a strong voice, effective eye contact with an audience, and a clear, logical presentation of ideas. You may use all or part of your class as an audience (check with your teacher), and for effect you might want half the group to dress up to resemble the Sharks, and the other half to resemble the Jets. The "authenticity" might help you get your message across.

Assignment: Pretend you are a young police officer who has just been assigned to the precinct where the Jets and Sharks are battling it out for control of the streets. You find this situation unacceptable and are sure that with some serious talk you can get both gangs to see that fighting and killing each other aren't nearly as beneficial as working together.

You decide to call a meeting, a Peace Council. You will speak on the "Advantages of Peace," and the rules are that no one will bring weapons of any kind and that everybody will sit silently till you are finished. Then they may challenge your ideas.

Build your speech to strongly persuade both sides to cooperate. You could put together your speech as follows:

a.   **Tell them the history of violence behind them—earlier conflicts that resulted in casualties and heartaches for all concerned.**

b.   **Advise them of the present situation. Clear things up for them. Tell them what they are doing from an "outsider's" point of view.**

c.   **Tell both gangs of the consequences of continuing their hostilities: jail, injury, and death.**

d.   **List the benefits of joining forces and doing good for themselves and their families and friends.**

e.   **Present some *alternatives* to their present way of doing business with each other. Suggest community projects, business opportunities, and social causes that they might get involved in *together* so as to ensure a safe future for themselves, their loved ones, and the City of New York.**

   Be bold. Be clear. And talk like you mean it.

17. West Side Story

Sentence Types

Groups of words that have subjects and predicates and that express a complete thought are called sentences. They come in four different types: declarative, imperative, exclamatory, and interrogative.

Declarative sentences make a statement: *Riff was the leader of the Jets.*
Imperative sentences express a command: *Come here.*
Exclamatory sentences express strong emotion: *I won't go!*
Interrogative sentences ask a question: *Was Bernardo their leader?*

Below are eighteen sentences. On the line next to each one, write a **D** if the sentence is declarative; write an **I** if the sentence is imperative; write an **E** if it is exclamatory; and write **Int** if it is interrogative.

1. _____ Be cool.

2. _____ We won!

3. _____ This is war!

4. _____ Can't you see that he's one of them?

5. _____ Can't you see that I'm in love?

6. _____ Chino has a gun!

7. _____ Without a gang, you're an orphan.

8. _____ Would you go to Doc's store for me?

9. _____ In America, anything is possible.

10. _____ Come to the rumble tonight.

11. _____ Why do you want to go back to Puerto Rico?

12. _____ Is Maria all right?

13. _____ They won't leave us alone.

14. _____ Take her home.

15. _____ Everything was going so well !

16. _____ Why do you kids live like there's a war on?

17. _____ Why do you kill?

18. _____ I feel that something good is going to happen.

17. West Side Story

Answers

Multiple Choice

(1) d (2) f (3) d (4) a (5) e (6) e (7) e (8) b (9) a (10) d

Pronouns/Verb Agreement

(1) was   (7) argues

(2) want/wants   (8) seems

(3) sings   (9) are

(4) love   (10) believes

(5) think   (11) was

(6) looks   (12) was

Oral Communication

Answers will vary.

Sentence Types

(1) I   (7) D   (13) D

(2) E   (8) Int   (14) I

(3) E   (9) D   (15) E

(4) Int   (10) I   (16) Int

(5) Int   (11) Int   (17) Int

(6) E   (12) Int   (18) D

18. ARSENIC AND OLD LACE

Author: Joseph Kesselring
Play Title: *Arsenic and Old Lace*
Director: Frank Capra

Running Time: 120 minutes
Year: 1944
Format: black and white

Summary

Mortimer Brewster, a drama critic and writer in his mid thirties, has two problems: he's just shattered his bachelor image by marrying Elaine Harper, the minister's daughter; and in sharing the shocking news with his aunts Abby and Martha, he has discovered they've poisoned and buried twelve men in their cellar. What to do?

Mortimer spends the entire plot of the story trying to keep this dastardly news from the police while trying to get his brother Teddy, who lives with Aunt Abby and Aunt Martha, committed to Happydale Rest Home. Teddy, who believes himself to be President Theodore Roosevelt, has been digging the Panama Canal in the cellar and has buried the aunts' "yellow fever" victims in the "locks."

Amidst this morbid confusion, Mortimer's other strange brother, Jonathan, returns with his sidekick, Dr. Einstein, a plastic surgeon who operates on criminals' faces to hide them from the peering eyes of the police. Jonathan demands a room and the use of Grandfather's old laboratory. He reminds Mortimer of the needles he used to insert under Mortimer's fingernails and threatens his aunts with his penchant for killing. To complicate matters, Jonathan and Einstein have brought their own body with them, that of a Mr. Spinalzo, who needs to be disposed of.

Mortimer remains unafraid of his sinister brother and threatens to tell the police of Jonathan's "baggage." But Einstein finds Teddy's "yellow fever victim" (Mr. Hoskins) in the cellar and blackmails Mortimer into silence. So now

Mortimer has three problems: to get Teddy committed; to protect his aunts from arrest and prison; and to get rid of Jonathan.

Meanwhile, Elaine Harper, Mortimer's bride who lives next door, keeps coming by to get him so they can leave for their honeymoon at Niagara Falls. The cab is waiting. Elaine is distraught. She is almost strangled by Jonathan at one point, and is tossed out the door by Mortimer at another. A fumbling police officer named O'Hara wants Mortimer to read a play he's written about his dance-hall mother, Peaches LaTour, and Mr. Witherspoon, the director of Happydale, wants Mortimer to read *his* play about life at the rest home.

In the midst of this, Mortimer ends up tied to a chair with the lights out and Jonathan pulling on rubber gloves to do a carving job on him. Dr. Einstein is nearby, sweating and complaining that he wants Jonathan to kill Mortimer the "quick way." Einstein and Jonathan are about to drink poisoned wine as a toast to the doomed Mortimer when O'Hara steps in and breaks it up. Shortly, other policemen arrive looking for O'Hara; then Lieutenant Rooney shows up, and after a brawl, arrests Jonathan.

The film ends with the aunts and Teddy being committed as a family to Happydale, and Mortimer being told that he is really *not* a Brewster (so he won't inherit their insanity). Mortimer runs out with his bride in his arms, kissing her to keep her from declaring her discovery that there *are* thirteen bodies buried in the basement.

18. Arsenic and Old Lace

Comprehension Quiz

Below are two exercises to check your comprehension. In the first exercise, write the letter of the character from the column at the right, on the line next to that character's description. Then, in the true-or-false exercise, write a plus sign (+) on the line next to true statements, and write a zero (0) next to false statements.

Section A. Matching

1. ___ a writer and critic   a. Mr. Hoskins

2. ___ a digger of the Panama Canal   b. Aunt Abby and Aunt Martha

3. ___ a plastic surgeon   c. Mortimer Brewster

4. ___ a sanatorium director   d. Elaine Harper

5. ___ a minister's daughter   e. Teddy Brewster

6. ___ a murdering monster   f. Jonathan Brewster

7. ___ kindly killers   g. Officer O'Hara

8. ___ a playwriting policeman   h. Einstein

9. ___ arsenic's twelfth victim   i. Mr. Spinalzo

10. ___ Jonathan's most recent victim   j. Mr. Witherspoon

Section B. True (+) or False (0)

1. ___ Mortimer Brewster is not really a Brewster.

2. ___ Aunt Abby and Aunt Martha are hired killers.

3. ___ Elaine lived next door to Jonathan Brewster all her life.

4. ___ At first Mortimer wants Teddy committed to Happydale because he thinks Teddy killed somebody.

5. ___ Mortimer discovers the first body while looking for his hat.

6. ___ Jonathan comes back home after twenty years to help Einstein set up a plastic surgery shop for criminals who are on the run.

7. ___ Jonathan used to torment Mortimer when they were boys.

8. ___ Jonathan's concern about his looks causes him to get arrested.

9. ___ Dr. Einstein helps criminals hide from the law by operating on their faces.

10. ___ Mortimer wants his aunts and his crazy brother to go to Happydale because he loves them and wants to protect them.

18. Arsenic and Old Lace

Comic Devices

Arsenic and Old Lace is funny, frightening, and farcical because of four techniques: **comic relief**—when something funny happens during or right after a tense scene; **slapstick**—ridiculous, clumsy actions such as falling over, tripping, and fumbling around; **close call**—when a serious incident *almost* occurs; and **wordplay**—when a word or phrase is used to make different, often humorous meanings.

Below are examples of these four techniques. Write CR next to the items that are examples of *comic relief*; write S next to examples of *slapstick*; write CC for *close call*; and write WP for *wordplay*. If necessary, use multiple letters to label items that illustrate more than one technique.

1. _____ Teddy hauls a dead body carefully down the stairs, then crashes to the bottom.

2. _____ Jonathan and Einstein are about to drink poisoned wine when Teddy blows his horn.

3. _____ Elaine says, "Niagara Falls!" and Mortimer answers, "Let it!"

4. _____ Mortimer runs for the door and nose-dives over a stuffed chair that's in the way.

5. _____ A stranger, Mr. Gibbs, comes to rent a room, and before he can drink poisoned wine, Mortimer screams and drives him out of the house.

6. _____ Teddy charges up the stairs and blows his horn, and Officer O'Hara drops the box of toys.

7. _____ Jonathan is about to strangle Elaine when Teddy comes up out of the cellar and says, "This is going to be a private funeral."

8. _____ Mortimer says, "Insanity runs in my family; in fact it practically gallops!"

9. _____ O'Hara says, "It's a great play; the first line will kill you."

10. _____ Jonathan is about to carve up Mortimer when Officer O'Hara rings the doorbell.

11. _____ Elaine slams the window shut on Mortimer's fingers.

12. _____ Teddy says, "Gentlemen, sit down!" (Jonathan and Einstein are already sitting.)

18. Arsenic and Old Lace

Verb Usage

Using verbs correctly is a skill that can be learned through regular prac-tice, like playing tennis or swimming the backstroke. In each sentence from *Arsenic and Old Lace* below, find the verb that is misused, then rewrite the sen-tence on the line provided, using the verb as it should be used. Underline the new verb(s) that you use in each sentence.

Example: Mortimer Brewster were a writer and drama critic.
Mortimer Brewster <u>was</u> a writer and drama critic.

1. "This were the home of my youth," Jonathan said to Einstein.

    _____

2. "It's time I come home and tooken care of you," Jonathan said to his aunts.

    _____

3. "If it's a secret proclamation, it have to be signed in secret," Teddy said.

    _____

4. "You can see that it gots to be done, don't you!" Jonathan said to Einstein.

    _____

5. "There's an elderly gentleman down there who seem to be very dead," said Jonathan.

    _____

6. "He thought he's Teddy Roosevelt," the officer said.

    _____

7. "When you made up your mind, you lose your head," Einstein said to Jonathan.

    _____

8. "You can't do this. This was developing into a very bad habit!" Mortimer said.

    _____

9. "I may be committed the wrong person," Judge Coleman said as Mortimer left the office.

    _____

10. "There is thirteen bodies buried in the basement!" Aunt Abby said.

    _____

18. Arsenic and Old Lace

Creative Writing

The old saying "Everybody's family tree has a nut on it somewhere!" is probably true. We all have a weird uncle or strange cousin who makes family gatherings "interesting," to say the least. On the lines below, tell about one of your relatives who seems "unique" in his or her own way. (This *does not* refer to people who are really mentally handicapped, but to folks who have some peculiar ways of behaving that are often funny or bizarre.) If you have no such relative, then write about a family scene—for example, a Christmas party or Thanksgiving dinner—in which such a character appears and causes all kinds of trouble. Have fun. Let your imagination get a workout.

18. Arsenic and Old Lace

Answers

Comprehension Quiz

Section A: (1) c (2) e (3) h (4) j (5) d (6) f (7) b (8) g (9) a (10) i

Section B: (1) + (2) 0 (3) 0 (4) + (5) 0 (6) + (7) + (8) + (9) + (10) +

Comic Devices

(1) CR, S

(2) CC, CR

(3) WP

(4) S

(5) CC, CR

(6) S

(7) CC, CR

(8) WP

(9) WP

(10) CC

(11) S

(12) CR

Verb Usage

1. "This *was* the home of . . ."

2. "It's time I *came* and *took* care of . . ."

3. "If it's a secret proclamation, it *has* to be . . ."

4. "You can see that *it's got* to be . . ."

5. "There's an . . . who *seems* to be . . ."

6. "He *thinks* he's . . ."

7. "When you *make* up your . . ."

8. "You can't do this. This *is* developing into . . ."

9. "I may be *committing* the wrong . . ."

10. "There *are* thirteen bodies . . ."

Creative Writing

Samples will vary.

19. ROMEO AND JULIET

Author: William Shakespeare
Play Title: *Romeo and Juliet*
Director: Franco Zeffirelli

Running Time: 139 minutes
Year: 1968
Format: color

Summary

A violent street fight between two families, the Capulets and Montagues, opens the first scene of the film. This feud is plaguing the otherwise refined city of Verona, Italy. The Prince issues a warning: Continue to fight on pain of death.

After the Prince's decree the crowds disperse and Juliet Capulet's father plans his annual community dance, to be held in the family ballroom. He invites a prospective bridegroom for Juliet: Paris, a gentleman and nobleman of the city.

At the party, Romeo Montague appears in a cat mask and is spied by Tybalt, a young Capulet hothead who tells Juliet's father. His reply: "Verona brags of him to be a virtuous and well-managed youth." Nothing violent happens. Later Romeo pulls Juliet behind a curtain and kisses her. By evening's end, the young lovers find that their last names make them enemies, but their love does not falter. Later, Romeo stands in the bushes and hears Juliet pine for him, "Romeo, Romeo, wherefore art thou Romeo?" They talk, plan marriage, and then part for the night.

Romeo sees Friar Lawrence and tells him of his love for Juliet. Juliet sends to her nurse to meet with Romeo and set the time and place for the wedding. The nurse complies because she thinks that Juliet is marrying Paris. Friar Lawrence marries the two youngsters, then they part. Romeo runs to tell his best friend, Mercutio, but meets Tybalt first. Tybalt wants a "quarrel" (sword fight), but Romeo tells him he has reasons to love him that he can't elaborate upon (he's family now, by marriage). Then Mercutio steps in to "quarrel" with Tybalt and is fatally stabbed in a rather frolicsome duel. Romeo loses control and kills Tybalt. He is summarily exiled by the Prince; Romeo cannot return to Verona or he will be executed.

Romeo and Juliet are devastated, but Friar Lawrence sets up a one-night tryst for them at the Capulet mansion with the help of the nurse. At daybreak, Romeo leaves for Mantua with plans to return. Meanwhile, Juliet's mother brings her the "happy news" that she is to marry the handsome and prosperous Paris on Thursday. Juliet erupts, swearing she'll do no such thing! Her father shoves her to the floor and says that she must get married, or leave the house.

Juliet seeks the counsel of Friar Lawrence, who tells her to go back home and tell her father that she'll marry Paris. Then, when she's alone in her room, she should drink a potion (which he quickly prepares for her) and be prepared to sleep for forty-two hours, during which time everyone will assume her dead. Then the Friar will notify Romeo with a letter that Juliet is thus indisposed, and the young lover will sneak into Verona and carry off his fourteen-year-old bride.

Juliet carries out the Friar's advice, and lies cold and asleep in a burial vault occupied by other Capulets, such as Tybalt. Romeo gets word that his beautiful wife is dead, and runs to find her prostrate on a slab of stone in the vault. He decides to kill himself so he can be with Juliet, and drinks poison. Friar Lawrence arrives and finds Romeo, realizes what has happened, and greets Juliet as she wakes from her drug-induced sleep. She sees Romeo and falls upon him, while the Friar leaves because the guards are coming (he hears their trumpets). Juliet is destroyed at the sight of Romeo, dead before her, and she takes his dagger and stabs herself in the chest.

The final scene is a speech given by the Prince. "You are all punished!" he shouts. And the crowd bow their heads before the bodies of their finest children, the star-crossed lovers, Romeo and Juliet.

19. Romeo and Juliet

Multiple Choice

Circle the letter of the correct answer for each item.

1. The main conflict between the Montagues and the Capulets is about:
(a) religion (b) money (c) politics (d) business (e) none of the above
(f) a, b, c, and d

2. Romeo tells only one person about his love for and vows to Juliet; it is:
(a) his father (b) his friend Benvolio (c) his friend Mercutio (d) Tybalt
(e) Friar Lawrence

3. Romeo meets Juliet at a: (a) baptism (b) revival (c) dance (d) wedding

4. Juliet's mother and father are arranging a marriage for her with:
(a) Benvolio (b) Tybalt (c) Paris (d) Mercutio

5. Juliet's secret ambition is to: (a) become a nun and serve Friar Lawrence
(b) marry Romeo (c) move to Paris (d) stop the fighting between the
families

6. Friar Lawrence agrees to marry the two lovers because: (a) he wants to
bring peace to the families (b) he is bound to by his duty as a priest (c) he
once did the same thing when he was 16 (d) he knows Juliet will hate him
for the rest of her life if he refuses

7. When Mercutio is stabbed he says: "You ask for me tomorrow and you
shall find me a grave man." He means: (a) he will take his fighting more
seriously after this (b) he will be dead (c) he is tired of being the town's
funny man (d) he will be digging his own grave

8. Mercutio's speech quoted above is an example of: (a) irony
(b) alliteration (c) foreshadowing

9. Juliet falls in love with Romeo almost immediately because: (a) she
admires his courage (b) some unknown force seems to draw them
together (c) she likes his cat mask (d) she is afraid of marrying Paris
(e) none of the above (f) all of the above

10. Romeo and Juliet's relationship is: (a) built more on passion than on
understanding (b) doomed (c) basically a secret (d) called "hopeless" by
Friar Lawrence (e) a, b, and c (f) b, c, and d (g) a, b, and d (h) none of
the above (i) all of the above

Name _____ Date _____

19. Romeo and Juliet

Vocabulary Update

Below is a list of words used in Shakespeare's original script of *Romeo and Juliet.* Accompanying each word is the modern definition: the word "hie," for example, means "hurry" in modern English.

For each original Shakespearean term, write a sentence about modern life using the Shakespearean word in place of the modern equivalent.

Example: "hie"—*I'm going to hie to the cafeteria to get a burrito.*

Shakespeare's word = Modern equivalent

1. **weeds** = clothes

   _____

2. **maw** = stomach

   _____

3. **teen** = sorrow

   _____

4. **chinks** = cash

   _____

5. **anon** = soon (in a minute)

   _____

6. **hie** = hurry

   _____

7. **humor** = mood

   _____

8. **knave** = scoundrel, creep

   _____

9. **wot** = know

   _____

10. **haply** = perhaps

   _____

19. Romeo and Juliet

Poetry

Read this boxed poem by Elizabeth Barrett Browning. Then write a response to the poem in the space provided below. You may wish to follow Mrs. Browning's lead and put your response in the form of a sonnet. Look up the word *sonnet* in a dictionary or in a reading textbook to learn what makes a sonnet a special type of poetic stanza.

When writing your response, think of someone you love. Can you "count the ways" in which you show love to this person? And the

> SONNET 43
>
> How do I love thee? Let me count the ways.
> I love thee to the depth and breadth and height
> My soul can reach, when feeling out of sight
> For the ends of Being and ideal Grace.
> I love thee to the level of every day's
> Most quiet need, by sun and candlelight.
>
> I love thee freely, as men strive for Right;
> I love thee purely, as they turn from Praise.
> I love thee with the passion put to use
> In my old griefs, and with my childhood's faith.
> I love thee with a love I seemed to lose
> With my lost saints—I love thee with the breath,
> Smiles, tears, of all my life!—and if God choose,
> I shall but love thee better after death.

ways in which this person loves you? What kinds of things—everyday comments, remarks, and gestures—do you exchange with each other? What kinds of things do you do for each other? What, after all, makes a good relationship, one that will last a lifetime?

19. Romeo and Juliet

Characterization

The broad cast of characters in *Romeo and Juliet* is made up of people with all sorts of different temperaments: Juliet is loyal and loving; Mercutio is witty and reckless. Beneath each of the adjectives given below, write the names of the characters who are well described by the adjective. (*Note:* You may list the same character under more than one adjective.)

**Romeo   Juliet   Tybalt   Mercutio   Juliet's father
Juliet's mother   Juliet's nurse   Friar Lawrence   The Prince**

Hot-tempered

1. _____
2. _____
3. _____
4. _____

Domineering

1. _____
2. _____
3. _____

Rude

1. _____
2. _____

Brave

1. _____
2. _____
3. _____
4. _____

Careless

1. _____
2. _____
3. _____
4. _____

Impulsive

1. _____
2. _____
3. _____
4. _____

Daring

1. _____
2. _____
3. _____
4. _____
5. _____

Wise

1. _____
2. _____

19. Romeo and Juliet

Answers

Multiple Choice

(1) e   (2) e   (3) c   (4) c   (5) b   (6) a   (7) b   (8) a   (9) b   (10) e

Vocabulary Update

Sentences will vary.

Poetry

Responses and sonnets will vary.

Characterization

Hot-tempered: Tybalt, Juliet's father, the Prince, Mercutio

Domineering: Juliet's father, Tybalt, Juliet's mother

Rude: Tybalt, Juliet's father

Brave: Romeo, Juliet, Tybalt, Mercutio

Wise: the Prince (or) Friar Lawrence

Careless: Mercutio, Romeo, Juliet, Tybalt

Impulsive: Romeo, Juliet, Mercutio, Tybalt

Daring: Juliet, Romeo, Friar Lawrence, Mercutio, Tybalt

20. THE BLACK STALLION

Author: Walter Farley
Novel Title: *The Black Stallion*
Director: Carroll Ballard

Running Time: 118 minutes
Year: 1979
Format: color

Summary

Alec Ramsey, a boy about 12 years old, is traveling with his father on a passenger ship, the *Drake*, off the North African coast. While on deck he hears a commotion and runs to find a magnificent black stallion being tormented by its captors. Later, he befriends the animal by bringing it sugar lumps.

That evening, Alec's father gives him a knife and a miniature replica of Alexander the Great's horse, Bucephalus, won in a card game aboard ship. When they retire for the night all is well. But the ship catches fire and sinks. The black stallion leaps into the sea and is tangled in the propeller. Alec cuts his ropes and the horse pulls him to safety. They are the only survivors of the *Drake*.

On a barren rocky island, Alec wakes to silence and emptiness. But he hears once again the tormented cries of the black stallion, and cuts the horse's ropes and harness, which have become entangled in the rocks. Later the Black saves Alec by stomping a cobra that was about to strike.

Alec learns to ride the Black, and they become friends. They understand each other. Eventually they are rescued by fishermen, and both horse and boy now head for America.

In town, the Black is restless. He runs off and Alec trails him to a farm owned by a man named Henry, an ex-racehorse trainer. Henry teaches Alec how to ride like a jockey and he times the Black, who is the fastest horse Henry has ever seen. Through a race promoter named Jim Neville, Henry sets up a match race between the Black, now called the "mystery horse," and two champions of speed, Cyclone and Sun Raider.

The black stallion starts poorly, being wild and unsure of the racetrack surroundings, but comes from way behind and wins. Alec, the "mystery rider," pulls off his mask toward the finish and the crowd roars its delight. As they cross the finish line Alec lets go his reins and rides as he did on the island, arms out, head up—one with the black stallion.

20. The Black Stallion

Multiple Choice

Circle the letter of the correct answer to each item.

1. The two major settings for the film are: (a) Paris, France, and Saudi Arabia (b) the sea and the wind (c) the island and Alec's homeland (d) the country and the city

2. Alec forms a bond with the Black through all of the following actions *except*: (a) giving the Black sugar cubes (b) opening the door to the Black's stall during the fire (c) killing the vicious trainer who whips and mistreats the Black (d) cutting the ropes that hold the Black to the propeller of the *Drake*

3. What does Alec receive from his father the night of the fire? (a) a model of Bucephalus (b) a wallet (c) a silver coin (d) a gold watch (e) a knife (f) both a and b (g) both c and d (h) both a and d (i) both a and e (j) both b and c

4. The Black saves Alec's life by: (a) winning the Kentucky Derby (b) rescuing Alec's father (c) towing the boy to shore (d) stomping a cobra to death (e) all of the above (f) both a and b (g) both a and c (h) both a and d (i) both b and c (j) both c and d

5. Alec is rescued from the island by: (a) soldiers (b) fishermen (c) a news team

6. Back home Alec is described as: (a) a nut (b) a pirate (c) a big thief (d) a hero

7. Henry is the perfect person to befriend Alec and the Black because: (a) he has no young son of his own (b) he loves horses (c) he has a farm (d) he used to be a jockey (e) all of the above (f) both a and b (g) both c and d (h) a, b, and d (i) a, c, and d

8. Alec's mother does not want him to ride the Black in the race because: (a) she had a dream that showed Alec dying (b) she knows it's a setup to get Henry back into racing (c) she doesn't trust Jim Neville, the race promoter (d) she thinks Alec is too young and could be killed (e) she doesn't trust the black stallion

9. The Black was not supposed to be able to race because: (a) he had no pedigree papers (b) he was too wild (c) he was hurt (d) he was untrained

20. The Black Stallion

Vocabulary

Below are ten words that pertain to the movie. Learn their definitions, then write each word in the sentence it best fits in.

desperate	**bellow**	**flounder(ed)**
sever(ed)	**parch(ed)**	**replica**
ordeal	**barren**	**melancholy**
	ruckus	

1. Alec discovered the black stallion when he heard a fierce _____ of stomping feet and cracking whips.

2. The black stallion _____ at the end of the rope, which was caught on the propeller of the *Drake*.

3. The horse was terrified and _____ for a way out of certain death by drowning.

4. Alec gave him new life when he dove underwater and _____ the rope that would have dragged the Black to the bottom of the sea.

5. When Alec woke from the _____, he was alone on the shore of a nameless, rocky island.

6. The space and silence made him _____.

7. The clothes on his back, the knife in his hand, and a miniature _____ of the legendary horse Bucephalus were the only things Alec had.

8. He was confused and hungry, and his throat was _____.

9. The island appeared to be _____ of all life.

10. Then he heard the _____ of the black stallion, and he knew he was not alone.

Name _____ Date _____

20. The Black Stallion

Quotations

You can tell when people speak in movies because their lips move and we hear their voices. But on paper it's not so easy. On paper the words spoken by a character have to be specially marked off by what are called quotation marks.

Example:　　　"I need this race," Henry said.

Quotation marks are placed around the spoken words. There are rules for placing the quotation marks next to other punctuation marks. The opening quotation mark (") is placed next to the first word of the quotation. The closing quotation mark (") follows a comma (,) or a period (.), and precedes a colon (:) or a semicolon (;). The above example shows a common pattern. A question mark (?) or exclamation point (!) is included inside the closing quote mark if the quoted words are a question or an exclamation.

Put quotation marks, capital letters, and correct punctuation in these lines from the film *The Black Stallion*.

1. he's too much horse for your boy　exclaimed Jake

2. squeeze my hand here　said Henry

3. what does the ball do　asked Alec

4. he's got speed he ain't even tapped yet　said Henry

5. don't lie to me　Mr. Daily　said Alec's mom

6. the Black is the mystery horse and I'm going to ride him　said Alec

7. what about his papers　Jake asked

8. he ain't got any　Henry answered

9 where'd you get this animal　Jim Neville asked

10. we're going to show everybody that the Black is the fastest horse in the world　Alec announced

20. The Black Stallion

Projects

There are many ways to respond to literature, written or filmed. Some people see a great movie and feel inspired to write a poem. Others get out their cameras and take pictures of scenes that reflect some of the emotions they felt while they watched the action unfold onscreen.

Below are some ideas you might use to make or do something that represents a moment, an idea, or a feeling expressed in the film *The Black Stallion*. Choose one, or come up with a project of your own; complete it, then present it to the entire class.

1. Sounds, as much as words, played an important role in *The Black Stallion*—the swish of waves on the island shore; the terrifying hiss of the killer cobra; the roar of the black stallion's breath and hooves as he pounded around the racetrack. Make a cassette tape recording of a collection of sounds that "speak" to the audience: sounds that show excitement; or sounds that soothe the listener; or sounds that are meant to frighten. Then play the cassette to the entire class. Ask for their reaction to see how effective your "sound track" was.

2. Music also played an important role in the movie *The Black Stallion*. When Alec rode the Black for the first time, we heard the dancing plink of piano keys, then the oboe, then violins, then the crash of drums as Alec and the Black exploded out of the sea. Make a cassette tape recording of excerpts from different songs you know that communicate one single emotion: loneliness, hope, joy, etc.

3. Write a song and play it for the class. Pretend you're writing an additional piece for the sound track of *The Black Stallion*. What will it sound like?

4. Write a legend of your own that involves a young boy or girl hero who does something extraordinary to gain the praises of a tribe or nation.

5. Write a poem, maybe your own "Ode to Alec Ramsey." Record a piece of music you like, and play it as background while you read the poem to the class.

6. Give an acceptance speech as if you were Alec and you were thanking the people at your school who honored you with a huge assembly.

7. Carve a model of the black stallion from wood or soap.

20. The Black Stallion

Answers

Multiple Choice

(1) c (2) c (3) i (4) j (5) b (6) d (7) e (8) d (9) a

Vocabulary

(1) ruckus   (6) melancholy

(2) floundered   (7) replica

(3) desperate   (8) parched

(4) severed   (9) barren

(5) ordeal   (10) bellow

Quotations (punctuation, capitalization)

1. "He's . . . boy!" exclaimed Jake.

2. "Squeeze . . . here," said Henry.

3. "What . . . do?" asked Alec.

4. "He's got . . . yet," said Henry.

5. "Don't . . . Mr. Daily," said Alec's mom.

6. "The Black is . . . him," said Alec.

7. "What about his papers?" Jake asked.

8. "He ain't got any," Henry answered.

9. "Where'd you get this animal?" asked Jim Neville.

10. "We're going . . . world!" Alec announced.

Projects

Projects will vary.

21. ANIMAL FARM

Author: George Orwell
Novel Title: *Animal Farm*
Director: John Halas

Running Time: 75 minutes
Year: 1955
Format: color cartoon

Summary

George Orwell's political fable involves a farmer named Jones who runs Manor Farm with a cruel hand. He has fallen on hard times and has taken to drink, which has made him even more oppressive toward his subjects, the animals with whom he makes his living.

One night after coming home drunk, Jones curses his animals and stumbles off to bed without feeding them. Old Major, the venerable resident pig, gathers all the animals together at a rally to say a few last words before he dies. "Overthrow Jones and we shall be rich and free. When you've gotten rid of Jones, don't adopt his ways . . . *All animals are equal!*"

Old Major dies and the animals revolt. They storm the storehouse and eat their fill. Then Jones appears, cracking his whip, but the animals don't cower; this time they attack and run Jones off the farm. The farm is theirs!

Jones organizes his fellow drunkards at the Red Lion tavern and they rush the farm in an attempt to conquer the animals, but they lose. The animals fight bravely—Boxer the draft horse, Benjamin the donkey, all the geese, sheep, goats, birds, and pigs—and repel the farmer's attack. Then the animals, led by two pigs, Snowball and Napoleon, proceed to Jones's house and destroy everything they can find. But Napoleon finds a litter of pups which he hides for later use. He alone stays in Jones's house while the rest of the animals shun such luxury.

The animals make laws: No Animal Shall Sleep In A Bed—No Animal Shall Drink Alcohol—Four Legs Are Good, Two Legs Bad—No Animal Shall Kill Another Animal—All Animals Are Equal. All the animals throw themselves into the work for the good of the farm, whose name they have changed to Animal Farm. They plant and harvest, and reap a bountiful crop. Snowball tells them to spread the news of freedom for animals, and the pigeons fly off with the message. Snowball teaches the animals to read and write. He tells them of his plan to bring power to the farm. "A light in every stall!" he says.

But Napoleon has a plan for bringing his own brand of power to the farm. He openly opposes Snowball at a rally and sics his vicious dogs on him. Snowball is murdered and Napoleon installs himself as ruler over all the animals: "I will take care of your interests," he says.

Napoleon changes the laws to fit his needs. He starts trade with the outside world, selling the hens' eggs just as Jones did. He executes traitors and moves all his pig associates into Jones's house. The farmers unite again for an assault on Animal Farm, but Napoleon is ready for them and urges the animals on from a safe place in the house. The farm is saved, but the windmill, Snowball's brainchild, is destroyed by dynamite at the hands of Jones himself.

It turns bitter cold and the animals must rebuild the windmill stone by stone, and with fewer rations and comforts than ever. Boxer is injured and is sold to the glue factory, and the pigs drink to his memory with liquor bought with Boxer's life. The corruption continues until Benjamin, Boxer's lifelong friend, organizes the animals to overthrow the pigs. In one scene, where Benjamin is looking into the window of Jones's house, he sees all the pigs standing on two legs and they appear to take on the face of Jones himself.

The last scene is the overthrow of Napoleon and his evil gang by all the animals of Animal Farm. The cycle is now complete, and we can only wonder who will rule Animal Farm from here on.

21. Animal Farm

True or False, and Why?

Mark the true statements with a plus sign (+). Mark the false statements with a zero (0) and explain briefly why each statement is false.

1. ____ Old Major counseled all the farm animals to overthrow Jones and take over the farm.

_____

2. ____ Snowball felt that the key to running the farm under the new system was to keep everyone ignorant.

_____

3. ____ The problem with the new plan of "animal rule" was that only one type of animal made most of the decisions.

_____

4. ____ Snowball was working on a plan to build a windmill that would provide power, so that the animals wouldn't have to work so hard.

_____

5. ____ Napoleon killed Snowball in a pistol duel because Snowball was caught trading with the outside world.

_____

6. ____ Napoleon secretly planted a bomb in the windmill and blew it away.

_____

7. ____ The animals gradually became wealthier and better fed under Napoleon's rule, and faithfully gave their time to build another windmill.

_____

8. ____ Boxer planned a revolt against Napoleon and eventually ran him off the farm.

_____

9. ____ The reason Napoleon lost the revolt against him was that his killer dogs were too intoxicated and lazy to protect him.

_____

10. ____ The story ends with Squealer being the next ruler of Animal Farm.

_____

21. Animal Farm

Personification

Personification is the technique of giving human characteristics to non-human things—animals, for instance. George Orwell, the writer of the novel on which the film *Animal Farm* was based, used animals to tell his story instead of real people. It must have been tough deciding which animals to put in different roles, such as the vicious ruler, the faithful workers, the assistant ruler, and the enforcers.

Beside each type of animal listed below, tell why you think Orwell chose that species of creature to play the part it did in the story. Why choose pigs to be the leaders and masterminds? Why choose a horse to play the role of tireless worker? Why is the donkey the sidekick and friend of the horse?

1. Pigs: _____
    _____

2. Horse: _____
    _____

3. Donkey: _____
    _____

4. Chickens: _____
    _____

5. Cows: _____
    _____

6. Geese: _____
    _____

7. Sheep: _____
    _____

8. Dogs: _____
    _____

9. Pigeons/Doves: _____
    _____

21. Animal Farm

Writing a Fable

George Orwell's *Animal Farm* is a fable. It is a fictional tale in which animals talk and act like humans. It ends with a strong, simple, instructive message that all should heed: "Absolute power corrupts absolutely."

Traditional fables, like those of Aesop, the great fable-writer of old, always carry a moral message that is true to life and basically wise. Aesop's fable of "The Fox and the Crow" is reprinted below. Read it, think about its moral message, then create your own simple fable that demonstrates a truth to live by. Write your fable on the lines below.

The Fox and the Crow

A Fox once saw a Crow fly off with a piece of cheese in its beak and settle on a branch of a tree. "That's for me, as I am a Fox," said Master Reynard (the Fox), and he walked up to the foot of the tree. "Good-day, Mistress Crow," he cried. "How well you are looking today—how glossy your feathers; how bright your eye. I feel sure your voice must surpass that of other birds, just as your figure does: let me hear but one song from you that I may greet you as the Queen of Birds." The Crow lifted up her head and began to caw her best, but the moment she opened her mouth the piece of cheese fell to the ground, only to be snapped up by Master Fox. "That will do," said he. "That was all I wanted. In exchange for your cheese I will give you a piece of advice for the future: *Do not trust flatterers.*"

_____

_____

_____

_____

_____

_____

_____

_____

_____

_____

21. Animal Farm

Answers

True or False, and Why?

(1) +

(2) 0; Snowball wanted everyone to be educated.

(3) +

(4) +

(5) 0; Snowball was killed by Napoleon's guard dogs so Napoleon could have all the power.

(6) 0; Jones blew up the windmill with dynamite.

(7) 0; The animals became poor and hungry under Napoleon's rule.

(8) 0; Boxer was shipped to the slaughterhouse by Napoleon.

(9) +

(10) 0; The animals once again have control of Animal Farm.

Personification

Answers will vary.

1. pigs—Pigs are known for being intelligent gluttons; they are stubborn and mean at times, too.
2. horse—Horses are powerful workers and symbolize trust and strength.
3. donkey—Donkeys are notoriously stubborn, and Benjamin finally stands up to Napoleon.
4. chickens—These creatures provide a product other than themselves to bring to market.
5. cows—Though not as intelligent as other creatures, cows have horns and can use them.
6. geese—The "talkers" on any farm, they warn of encroaching danger and can fight.
7. sheep—These are docile creatures with few weapons except for rams' horns.
8. dogs—Known for being fierce killers, they use their canine teeth to rip and tear.
9. pigeons/doves—Traditionally they are message-carriers who can cover great distances quickly.

Fable

Samples will vary.

22. A RAISIN IN THE SUN

Author: Lorraine Hansberry
Play Title: *A Raisin in the Sun*
Director: Bill Duke

Running Time: 171 minutes
Year: 1988
Format: color

Summary

A Raisin in the Sun is filmed as a play in three acts with all the action taking place in the apartment of the Youngers, a black family. Lena Younger, the matriarch, is a strong-willed, dominating woman who is about to receive a $10,000 check from the life insurance company that insured her husband, the late "Big Walter." The plot revolves around how the various family members believe in the money as their individual salvation: Walter Junior wants the money to invest in a liquor store; Ruth, Walter's wife, wants a house and a life away from the ghetto; and Walter's sister, Beneatha, wants to finish medical school and "make something of herself."

In the opening scene Walter wakes to another day as a rich white man's chauffeur. He grimaces in the mirror, then proceeds to the kitchen, where he talks of his big plans to open a liquor store with two buddies, Bobo and Willie. Ruth, his wife, will have none of it. She won't listen to his big ideas, and that sets the scene for one of the main conflicts in the film—Walter is alone in his dream to be something, to have money, to be a successful businessman.

Walter teases bitterly and fights with his sister Beneatha, who is a bright, attractive 20-year-old with prospects for a successful future. She wants to "express herself"—find some purpose in life that will ennoble her efforts in school, and later, in her career.

At the center of the turmoil is Momma, Lena Younger, the mother who raised her two children in a time of extreme poverty and racism, who wants the simple things for her family—a house, a job, and enough money to buy the clothes and food necessary for survival. She feels none of the inner struggle for something "better" that Walter Junior and Beneatha so desperately feel.

The generations continue to clash till Lena finally relents and hands over $6,500 to her son with the pronouncement that he is the "head of the house." (She has put $3,500 down on a house in an all-white suburb called Clyborne Park, and she asks Walter to put $3,000 in a savings account for Beneatha.)

Walter immediately "invests" all $6,500 with his friends Willie and Bobo and loses it all; Willie never showed up to close the deal. Walter is devastated. He decides to call the president of the Clyborne Park Welcoming Committee and to accept the man's offer to buy back the house at a profit to the Younger family.

When the man arrives, Momma Younger presents Travis to her son and says, "Teach him what Willie taught you." Walter can't go through with it. He can't teach his son the demeaning ways of the white/black world, and tells Mr. Lindner that his family is proud—simple, but proud, and they *will* move into the house in Clyborne Park because it is his father's legacy to the family; "He built it brick by brick," Walter says. And with that Momma says, "He became a man today."

The movie closes with Momma Younger taking her only houseplant with her as she leaves the old apartment. She will establish it in a garden in a new place, a place of hope and opportunity for the new generation who will build a different world for blacks and for all people.

22. A Raisin in the Sun

Multiple Choice

Circle the letter of the correct answer for each item.

1. Where does the Younger family live? (a) in an apartment in Chicago (b) in a house in the Bronx (c) in a mobile home in Atlanta (d) in an apartment in Baltimore

2. Momma Younger gets a $10,000 check from the insurance company because: (a) her old apartment burned (b) her mother left her an inheritance (c) her husband died

3. Who are Walter's "business associates"? (a) Frank and Adeline (b) Hal and Weasel (c) Pete and Benney (d) Willie and Bobo

4. What is Walter Younger's big dream? (a) to be a chauffeur (b) to own a liquor store (c) to own a bottling manufacturing plant (d) to buy a house in the suburbs

5. What is Beneatha Younger's dream? (a) to be a teacher (b) to marry a rich man (c) to have a home in the suburbs (d) to graduate from college with a degree in medicine

6. What is Ruth Younger's dream? (a) to be a teacher of the deaf (b) to own a home in the suburbs (c) to have money to buy food (d) to be a doctor

7. How does Walter lose most of the family's money? (a) bets on the horses at the Clyborne Park Raceway (b) invests it in a business with Willie Harris (c) loses it on the last roll of the dice at the Green Hat Bar (d) gives it to Travis

8. What does Momma Younger do for the family with some of the money? (a) buys an apartment on the Upper West Side (b) invests in a hair-styling business (c) sends Travis to medical school (d) buys a house

9. Why does Beneatha call the rich and handsome George Murchison a fool? (a) he believes that money is more important than ideas (b) he believes that college is worthless (c) he believes that Walter is a solid businessman with good ideas (d) he has made a large investment in Walter's dream

10. The Clyborne Park Welcoming Committee wants to buy back the Youngers' house because: (a) they don't want blacks in their neighborhood (b) they want only apartment buildings in their subdivision (c) they don't think the Youngers will be able to afford it

22. A Raisin in the Sun

Predictions

Reading literature can stretch your imagination if you let it. Think about the characters in *A Raisin in the Sun* and imagine their lives *after* they go off the screen. What happens to each of them in the following ten, twenty, or even forty years? On the lines provided write your predictions for each of the five main characters in the movie.

Momma Younger—How will she live out the last years of her life? What changes will she encounter?

_____

_____

_____

Walter Younger—What will he do for work? What plans will he have? Where will he succeed? Where will he fail?

_____

_____

_____

Beneatha Younger—Will she become a doctor? Will she leave Chicago?

_____

_____

_____

Travis Younger—Who will be his friends? What will school be like? Will he go to college?

_____

_____

_____

Ruth Younger—Will she become the next "Momma Younger"? Will she find true happiness in the suburbs? What problems will she experience? What joys?

_____

_____

_____

22. A Raisin in the Sun

Poetry

At right is a poem by Langston Hughes. It is about dreams, about those far-off visions of things we picture in our minds when we think about the future. Read the poem and think about what it says about dreams and how important they are. Then think about the people in the Younger family—Walter, Ruth, Beneatha, Travis, and Momma. How do their lives compare to the broken-winged bird in Langston Hughes's poem? What happened when Walter lost his dream? How did he handle it? What did he do next? What was Ruth's dream? Did she see it come true? What dreams does Momma have? Travis? Beneatha? Write a short essay about one or more of these dreamers, incorporating imagery from the Hughes poem.

> ### *Hold Fast to Dreams*
>
> *Hold fast to dreams,*
> *For if dreams die,*
> *Life is a broken-winged bird*
> *That cannot fly.*
>
> *Hold fast to dreams*
> *For if dreams go*
> *Life is a barren field*
> *Frozen with snow.*

22. A Raisin in the Sun

Essay

At one point Beneatha asks George Murchison, "Why read books? Why go to school?" George replies, "You read books to learn facts to get grades, to pass the course, to get a degree. It has nothing to do with thoughts!"

Write a brief essay in which you either defend George's opinion or oppose it. On the first few lines tell what you believe is the overall reason that people read books and attend schools and colleges. Then write two or three paragraphs that support your view, using examples from your own life and from the lives of people you know.

22. A Raisin in the Sun

Answers

Multiple Choice

(1) a   (2) c   (3) d   (4) b   (5) d   (6) b   (7) b   (8) d   (9) a   (10) a

Predictions

Answers will vary.

Poetry

Sample essay:

Dreams are the essence of life, says the poet Langston Hughes. Without dreams human-kind is as trapped as a flightless bird, as lifeless as a barren field. In *A Raisin in the Sun*, we see this idea supported by the lives of those in the Younger family, who all have reason to want something better, something more out of life.

Walter is a man with the pride his father instilled in him, but with no way to exercise it. He believes he needs to be a businessman with money and contacts and chauffeur-driven cars. He doesn't get what he has dreamed about, but he does achieve something of great value; he learns that his father's life, and thus his, is not a waste. He can be a chauffeur and still be a man. Once he gains this understanding, one gets the feeling that Walter will be able to "fly" free of the chains of envy and self-pity that have kept him bent under a dream that was doomed from the start.

Beneatha is another dreamer in the story whose future looks as bleak as a cold, barren field of snow, once she learns how Walter has squandered her college money on an ill-conceived scheme. But she learns that Walter loves her, that the Youngers are a family, in the full sense of the word. And one gets the impression that Beneatha will be better for new understanding and will be able to live a more fruitful life no matter what the future holds for her.

All the Youngers want something, and in the end get more than they realized was possible—a better understanding of who they are as a family. And from here on we can imagine them growing stronger and more "human" in their struggle to survive and live out their dreams.

Essay

Essays will vary.

23. REAR WINDOW

Author: Cornell Woolrich
Novel Title: *Rear Window*
Director: Alfred Hitchcock

Running Time: 113 minutes
Year: 1954
Format: color

Summary

Rear Window opens with a view through the apartment window of newspaper photographer L. B. Jefferies. There's a courtyard below, surrounded by dozens of other apartments whose rear windows all face in toward each other. We see glimpses of people living their daily lives as the camera slowly pans across the various windows till it pulls back in to Jefferies' room and focuses on his sweaty, snoozing face; he is propped in a chair, his leg in a cast. His broken camera lies on the table beneath a picture of the auto racetrack crash that injured him, which hangs near a photo of a beautiful young woman—his rich and proper girlfriend, Lisa Freemont.

Other characters in the film form a backdrop for Hitchcock's "stage" metaphor: the frustrated musician who composes and plays beautiful pieces all through the film; the lonely alcoholic woman who lives in the misery of her own company; the chubby sculptor who creates works of art called "Hunger"; the older couple whose friendly little dog is their only family; the young married couple; the beautiful dancer who lives directly below the sinister jewelry salesman and his invalid wife. We meet these people by watching with Jefferies through his apartment window. We are as bored as he is, till we witness the jewelry salesman leaving his apartment several times on a rainy night toting his metal sample case. When his wife fails to reappear, a mystery is afoot whose solution is obvious: the salesman killed his ailing wife and cut her up with a saw and knife and hauled her out in pieces.

The drama is built around Jefferies' infectious conviction that the salesman committed murder under the noses of dozens of people without raising an eyebrow of interest. Jefferies' girlfriend, Lisa Freemont, first gets caught up in the mystery by watching Thorwald, the killer/salesman, through the same rear window. Then the insurance nurse, Stella, becomes convinced that Thorwald has killed his wife. (Stella's sick humor is quintessential Hitchcock and makes the film a model of what this brilliant director of horror films can do.) The only one who refuses to believe Jefferies' murder theory is his friend, Doyle, a local detective.

Jefferies must have evidence in order to convince Doyle, so Lisa and Stella sneak into the flower garden and dig where the neighbor's little dog had been sniffing around, but find nothing. Then Lisa, in a dash of spirit, decides to climb the fire escape into Thorwald's apartment to find his wife's wedding ring. She finds it, but Thorwald catches her. Jefferies and Stella watch in horror as Thorwald assaults Lisa. The police, alerted by Jefferies, show up and arrest Lisa. But before she is taken out of the apartment, she flashes the ring on her finger toward Jefferies' window.

Thorwald sees which window she's signaling to and proceeds to track down Jefferies and attempt to kill him. In desperation Thorwald shoves Jefferies out the same window through which Thorwald's evil deed was discovered. The police arrive, arrest Thorwald, and get Jefferies some medical attention.

The final scene shows Jefferies asleep, as in the opening scene, but with two broken legs and Lisa Freemont reclining nearby, reading an adventure novel, then putting it down and picking up a fashion magazine. She has found a way to impress the adventurous, hard-living photographer with her derring-do, and now, we surmise, she will be able to convince Jefferies that their marriage will work.

23. Rear Window

Plot Sequence

The events that make up the movie *Rear Window* are listed briefly below. But they are not in the correct sequence. Find the event that happened first and place the letter **A** on the corresponding line; then find the event that happened second and place the letter **B** on the line, and so forth, until all the events are lettered in the correct order from **A** to **P**.

1. _____ Jefferies, with two broken legs, lies asleep in a chair.

2. _____ Lisa rests next to Jefferies, reading an adventure novel and then a fashion magazine.

3. _____ Lisa is arrested for breaking and entering.

4. _____ Lisa is caught by Thorwald as she searches his apartment for Mrs. Thorwald's ring.

5. _____ Jefferies hears a scream and the sound of breaking glass.

6. _____ Lisa goes to Thorwald's apartment building and gets his name and address from his mailbox in the lobby.

7. _____ Thorwald leaves his apartment in the middle of the night, in the rain, carrying his metal sample case.

8. _____ Jefferies sends Thorwald a note: "What have you done with her?"

9. _____ The neighbor's dog is strangled.

10. _____ Lisa shows Mrs. Thorwald's wedding ring to Jefferies, from the window of Thorwald's apartment.

11. _____ Thorwald leaves his apartment with a woman other than his wife.

12. _____ It's hot, humid, and boring and Jefferies says to Stella, "I'd welcome trouble about now."

13. _____ Lisa orders dinner delivered to Jefferies' apartment from the 21 Club, a posh restaurant in New York City.

14. _____ Stella and Lisa dig in the garden where the dog has been digging.

15. _____ Thorwald dumps Jefferies out the window.

16. _____ Jefferies uses bright flashbulbs to blind Thorwald temporarily.

23. Rear Window

Spelling

Below are ten words that end with the letters "-ial," which means "having to do with" or "pertaining to." The word *Presidential* means "pertaining to the President"; the word *residential* means "having to do with where people reside or live." You could say, for example: "The fire was in a residential area," meaning, where homes are located, not downtown in the business district.

Write the spelling word from the list below that best completes each sentence. You may write the word several times on the back of this page for practice before taking a quiz, or you may want to spell the words into a tape recorder and listen to the playback just before the quiz. Use a dictionary to find the meanings of any words you don't know.

trivial	jovial	bestial	mercurial	congenial
artificial	menial	impartial	official	beneficial

1. Stella had the _____ task of massaging Jefferies' back several times a week.

2. Stella was quite _____ in the face of what she realized had actually happened in Thorwald's apartment.

3. At first everyone thought that L. B. Jefferies' bits of evidence were _____ and of no real importance.

4. Thorwald's behavior seems _____ when you consider what he did.

5. Jefferies' emotions became more _____ as he got closer and closer to proving that Thorwald was a murderer.

6. Doyle could be called an _____ observer in the case, since he wasn't really emotionally involved.

7. Lisa's efforts to prove that Thorwald was the killer were very _____ because in the end it was she who found the evidence that exposed him.

8. The _____ word from the police department was that Thorwald was innocent.

9. Thorwald didn't sell real jewelry; he sold _____, costume jewelry that imitated the real thing.

10. After all the arguing that went on between Lisa and L. B. Jefferies, the movie ends on a _____ note, with Lisa reading while Jefferies sleeps the sleep of the victorious in his favorite chair.

23. Rear Window

Vocabulary

Below are ten vocabulary words that pertain to the movie *Rear Window*. Look up these words in a dictionary, then write the word that best completes each sentence on the line provided.

homicidal   irrational   nocturnal   pivotal   hypothetical
factual   ethical   unusual   practical   mutual

1. L. B. Jefferies struggled with the question of whether what he was doing with his binoculars was truly _____.

2. Right from the beginning, Doyle thought Jefferies' conclusions about Thorwald were completely _____, because logically, a killer would not murder someone in front of an open window.

3. Jefferies admitted that his conclusions were _____, because he had no hard evidence, but he still insisted he was right about Thorwald.

4. It turned out, of course, that Thorwald was a _____ maniac.

5. Thorwald's _____ comings and goings with the sample case first got Jefferies' attention.

6. Doyle wanted _____ evidence, not some hypothetical theory about what Thorwald might have done.

7. The movie's _____ scene was when Lisa found the ring and showed it to Jefferies, who was watching from his window, and Thorwald realized who had been spying on him.

8. Lisa set aside her _____ nature and let her emotions take over when she climbed that fire escape to Thorwald's apartment.

9. Probably for the first time since they fell in love, Lisa and L. B. Jefferies shared a _____ goal as they worked to prove that Thorwald was a murderer.

10. Director Hitchcock's greatest strength is putting his unsuspecting characters in _____ situations and watching them react in daring, creative ways.

23. Rear Window

Predictions

An important skill to practice when viewing a movie is to predict what would have happened if certain things about the story had been changed. This is called "Predicting the What-If's." If Jefferies had been blinded instead of laid up with a broken leg, how would the story have developed? What would Hitchcock, the director, have had to do to make the story work? Would he have needed to bring in other characters? What kinds of characters?

Predicting gives you a chance to work with events, create new situations, and ponder them as if you were the writer or director. On the lines below each "What-If," write out a brief prediction of events. Tell what difference you think the change in circumstances would have made in the plot of *Rear Window*.

1. What if Jefferies had been a librarian, rather than a photographer?

   _____

   _____

2. What if Doyle had believed Jefferies from the start?

   _____

   _____

3. What if the police had not arrived in time to arrest Lisa?

   _____

   _____

4. What if Thorwald had pulled his curtains and kept them shut?

   _____

   _____

5. What if the story had taken place in the suburbs instead of in a crowded apartment complex?

   _____

   _____

6. What if Stella had been Thorwald's secret lover?

   _____

   _____

23. Rear Window

Answers

Plot Sequence

(1) O   (5) C   (9) G   (13) B

(2) P   (6) F   (10) K   (14) I

(3) L   (7) D   (11) E   (15) N

(4) J   (8) H   (12) A   (16) M

Spelling

1. menial
2. jovial
3. trivial
4. bestial
5. mercurial
6. impartial
7. beneficial
8. official
9. artificial
10. congenial

Vocabulary

1. ethical
2. irrational
3. hypothetical
4. homicidal
5. nocturnal
6. factual
7. pivotal
8. practical
9. mutual
10. unusual

Predictions

Answers will vary.

24. TO SIR, WITH LOVE

Author: E. R. Braithwaite
Book Title: *To Sir, with Love*
Director: James Clavell

Running Time: 105 minutes
Year: 1967
Format: color

Summary

On his first day at North Quay Secondary School in London, Mr. Mark Thackary, a black, sophisticated, unemployed engineer, looks in on the class he will teach once he accepts the position as replacement for one Mr. Hackman. The students are smoking, laughing, tossing paper, and throwing smug looks his way as he quickly shuts the door and heads for the teachers' lounge. The year has begun.

He meets Grace Evans, the deputy head teacher; Mr. Weston, the weary cynic who advises Thackary to leave while he can; and four ladies who teach at North Quay, including the beautiful Jillian Blanchard, another first-year teacher. The school is made of "rejects from other schools," the principal tells Thackary; they live hard lives in the poorer section of London.

Thackary tries traditional lessons for a few weeks while the students slam desks, drop books, saw the legs off his desk, and burn panties in the coal-burning stove. Thackary finally loses his temper and storms out of the room, only to return shortly with an inspired idea. "We are going to act like adults and you will treat each other like adults. Books are out. They are useless to you!"

Thackary proceeds to educate his students in the ways of "survival"; he teaches them to make salads, enter rooms politely, and to appreciate art and history through an unprecedented field trip to a local museum.

But things don't stay low-key for long. Pamela Dare, a pretty blond student, falls in love with him. An overweight boy in class, Buckley, gets hurt by a physical education teacher who has been picking on him for years. A boy named Potter goes after a teacher (Mr. Bell) with a chunk of wood. The principal cancels all future field trips.

The mother of a black student named Seals dies, and the class takes up a collection for flowers, but ignores Thackary's attempt to contribute. The class refuses to deliver the flowers in person to the black section of London in order to avoid gossip, but Pamela Dare agrees to go. Then Thackary counsels Miss Dare to "grow up" and forgive her mother and make peace. Miss Dare resents his intrusion into her life. One day the class tough-guy, Denham, challenges Thackary with boxing gloves in the gym. But here the tide finally turns. Thackary knocks the wind out of Denham with one punch to the belly, and suddenly Denham respects Thackary's sense of fair play—"You could have done me in," he says.

From then on things go Thackary's way: He gets an offer for an engineering job at a radio plant, he is invited to the class's end-of-the-year party, he attends Seals's mother's funeral and finds the entire class, led by Miss Dare, standing on the sidewalk holding flowers, waiting for him.

The last scene is a dance where a special number is requested—ladies' choice. Pamela Dare dances with Mr. Thackary, and then Miss Peg ("Babs") sings the theme song, "To Sir, with Love." The class thanks Mr. Thackary, gives him a wrapped gift, then asks for a speech. Thackary can't respond. He says, "I'd better go and put this away."

While he's momentarily alone in his classroom, a pair of ruffians charge into the room. One picks up his new pewter mug, slams it on the desk, and says, "We're in your bloody class next term!" They run out. Thackary stands and rips up the envelope containing his new job offer. Thackary will stay and teach. As Mr. Weston said, "Anybody can be an engineer."

24. To Sir, with Love

Direct Quotations

When you write the exact words that someone speaks, you must do the following:

1. Capitalize the first letter of the first word spoken.
2. Put all punctuation that belongs to the quoted words inside the quotation marks.

Below are statements made by the characters in the movie *To Sir, with Love*. Punctuate and capitalize each quote, then identify the speaker of each quote by writing the letter of each character from the list below on the line provided. *Note*: Some characters are quoted more than once.

A = Mr. Thackary B = Mr. Weston C = Mr. Bell D = Pamela Dare
E = Denham F = Babs G = Potter H = Seals I = Jillian Blanchard

1. ____ its encouraging that you know so little and are so easily amused. I can look forward to a happy time

2. ____ they will become part of the great London unwashed—illiterate, smelly, and quite content

3. ____ i hate my father

4. ____ there's something frightening but at the same time challenging about this school

5. ____ dancing is merely their way of keeping fit for the more amusing pastime of teacher baiting

6. ____ do you two shake

7. ____ i believe one should fight for what one believes, provided one is absolutely sure one is absolutely right

8. ____ are you a man or a hoodlum

9. ____ if you want to dance with me you bleedin' well better ask proper

10. ____ look at me. I'm a lady I am

11. ____ it is your duty to change the world if you can

12. ____ marriage is no way of life for the weak, the selfish, or the insecure

13. ____ i don't expect to be taught manners by those morons

14. ____ don't worry about your desk sir. I'll tidy it every day

15. ____ most of us have been up in front of the law

24. To Sir, with Love

Vocabulary

The eleven words below are used often in the movie *To Sir, with Love.* Try to recall lines from the film that used the words in the list. If you could remember even half of them, you'd be doing well. Videos aren't as easy to refer back to as books are, so you may want to ask your teacher to play sections of the film again.

Study the eleven vocabulary words and their meanings. Then write a paragraph using at least six of the words.

quay	wharf
cockney	language of the people from the East End of London
fancy	(v.) to like, to be partial toward; (n.) a liking, an affection
skinned	broke, penniless
toff	upper-class, mannered gentleman
barrow	career
shake	(v.) to dance
hiding	(n.) a beating
"talk posh"	to use proper language
daft	(adj.) crazy, simpleminded
ta	good-bye

n. = noun   v. = verb   adj. = adjective

24. To Sir, with Love

Short Answers

One of the strong points of the movie *To Sir, with Love* is the relationship Mr. Thackary develops with his students. Read the questions below and write your answers on the lines provided.

1. The relationship between Mr. Thackary and his class goes from "very hostile" at the beginning of his term as replacement teacher, to "very supportive and friendly" by the end of the term. What are some specific things that Mr. Thackary did to make this radical change possible?

   _____

   _____

   _____

   _____

2. What can you learn from Mr. Thackary's experience that might help you in building positive relationships with other people in your own life?

   _____

   _____

   _____

   _____

3. Think of someone with whom you want to get along better. What specific things could you do to improve this relationship?

   _____

   _____

   _____

   _____

4. What actions can you take if things don't go smoothly right away in the relationship, once you begin working to improve it?

   _____

   _____

   _____

   _____

24. To Sir, with Love

Short Story

In the movie *To Sir, with Love,* grades are never talked about. What if you were to attend a school where everyone got A's in every class, from Advanced Math to Art 101? What would it be like to be a student in such a place? How would a guaranteed A change your attitude toward schoolwork, choice of classes, and your future plans? How would this grading policy affect your relationship with your teachers? Your friends?

Write a short story below about your first day in Straight A School. You may speak in the first person ("I") or the third person ("he" or "she").

24. To Sir, with Love

Answers

Direct Quotations

1.	A	"It's . . . time."
2.	B	"They . . . content."
3.	H	"I hate my father!"
4.	I	"There's . . . school."
5.	B	"Dancing . . . baiting."
6.	D	"Do . . . shake?"
7.	A	"I . . . right."
8.	A	"Are . . . hoodlum?"
9.	F	"If . . . proper!"
10.	F	"Look . . . am!"
11.	A	"It . . . can."
12.	A	"Marriage . . . insecure."
13.	B	"I . . . morons!"
14.	D	"Don't . . . day."
15.	F	"Most . . . law."

Vocabulary

Sample paragraph:

Mr. Thackary, a young, black engineer, hires on to teach at North *Quay* School. He is called a "*toff*" by the students, who all use the rough-and-ready *cockney* dialect to communicate with each other. Thackary's problems are many, including the affections of one of his students, Pamela Dare, who has taken a *fancy* to him. She asks him early on if he *shakes*, and Thackary, embarrassed, leaves the room. However, by the end of the film she persuades him to dance with her one time before the term ends. In a moving final scene, Thackary gives up his *barrow* as an engineer and stays on as a teacher at North Quay.

Short Answers

1. Sample:

   Mr. Thackary, after realizing the environment in which he was teaching, developed a new approach to working with the students of North Quay. He ignored the textbooks and taught the kids what they really needed to know—survival skills. He got involved in their personal lives when they needed him, and he always treated them with the utmost respect.

2–4. Answers will vary.

Short Story

Answers will vary.

25. THE MAN THAT CORRUPTED HADLEYBURG

Author: Mark Twain
Short Story Title: "The Man That Corrupted Hadleyburg"
Director: Ralph Rosenblum

Running Time: 40 minutes
Year: 1980
Format: color

Summary

A stranger, whose name is never given, returns to Hadleyburg with a sack of gilded coins and a plan; he aims to teach Hadleyburg a lesson in the subjects of temptation, artificial honesty, and arrogance. It seems that the stranger was in Hadleyburg once before, but got a poor reception. He was a gambler and he was broke. Evidently he was asked to leave in no uncertain terms.

Upon entering Hadleyburg, the stranger visits with the outcast minister, the Reverend Burgess, who, since losing his congregation because of an offensive sermon, sits in the town square and whittles wood to pass the time. The Reverend points toward the home of Edward Richards, about whom the stranger has inquired. The stranger knocks on the Richards' door carrying his sack, which weighs 99 pounds, 4 ounces. The stranger tells Edward and Mary Richards his story: he was hungry and destitute when he was last in town and a kind man gave him twenty dollars and some advice. He wants now to find the man and reward his simple generosity with forty thousand dollars in gold. The best way to do this, he contends, is to announce in the town paper, *The Censor*, that if anyone can quote the piece of advice given to the stranger by the kind citizen of Hadleyburg, then that person should receive the gold. The stranger leaves the sack of coins in the care of Edward and Mary, and walks out the door.

The Richards do publish the stranger's request, but not before being tormented by the temptation to say nothing and abscond with the money. And the torment doesn't end with the Richards family; the stranger writes each of the 19 prominent families in town a letter saying that Barclay Goodson, before he died, told the stranger of a kind deed done by *them* unto him (Goodson) and thus the "gold" must go to them in Goodson's absence. The stranger shares Goodson's word of advice with each family: "You are far from being a bad man; go and reform." Each family is to write the secret message in a letter to Reverend Burgess, who is then to read each letter in public at a town meeting.

Each family, including Edward and Mary Richards, writes a letter to Reverend Burgess, each letter containing the same secret message: "You are far from being a bad man; go and reform."

A few days later when Reverend Burgess reads the letters at the town meeting the crowd becomes irate. Howls of scorn fill the church. But then there is a sudden silence. Only 18 letters have been read, and everyone knows there are 19 prominent families. Who has not been heard from?

Edward Richards rises from his chair to confess, and says, "Mary and I feel that we are as guilty as the rest." The Reverend Burgess immediately acknowledges Edward's generous spirit and nods at him to sit and keep quiet. Upon hearing this, the crowd instantly appoints Edward and Mary the sole guardians of the sack, and then they cry for the sack to be opened.

Upon untying the sack the hoax is revealed, and the "19'ers" are left staring at a sack of "gilded disks of lead" for which they sacrificed their honor and standing in the eyes of the townspeople and the world.

The stranger steps out of the story and says with a satisfied smile: "It's an honest town again. A man would have to rise early to catch 'em napping now!"

25. The Man That Corrupted Hadleyburg

True or False

Mark the true statements with a plus sign (+), and the false statements with a zero (0).

1. _____ The stranger's motive for the trick he played on Hadleyburg was revenge.

2. _____ The stranger believes that honesty is false unless it has been tested by the chance to be dishonest.

3. _____ The "19'ers" were all members of the same civic orchestra in Hadleyburg.

4. _____ No one gave the stranger any money on his first visit to Hadleyburg.

5. _____ Hadleyburg was a word that meant the same as "incorruptible."

6. _____ The remark made to the stranger never really was made at all.

7. _____ The town newspaper was called *The Censor*.

8. _____ Barclay Goodson was actually a social outcast who hated Hadleyburg and all that it stood for.

9. _____ Mr. Richards was chosen by the stranger because the stranger knew that Richards would not run off with the bag of gold.

10. _____ Reverend Burgess was put in charge of the letters and the town meeting because he was rich and had nothing to gain by stealing the gold.

11. _____ What Barclay actually said to the stranger was: "You are far from being a bad man; go and reform."

12. _____ All 19 families handed in a letter containing the same saying.

13. _____ Reverend Burgess did not read Mr. Richards' letter because Mr. Richards had done the Reverend a favor by warning him of trouble.

14. _____ Mr. and Mrs. Richards are hailed as honest, which, in fact, they are.

15. _____ Barclay Goodson was dead by the time the stranger returned.

16. _____ Reverend Burgess was one of the few people in Hadleyburg who had taken the time to talk to Barclay Goodson.

25. The Man That Corrupted Hadleyburg

Vocabulary

Using a dictionary, write a brief definition for each of the numbered words below. Then write the name of a character from the movie *The Man That Corrupted Hadleyburg* to whom each word *most likely* applies. (Some names could be used more than once, others not at all.)

Example: greed: *excessive desire; especially for wealth—Mr. Wilson*

1. envy: _____

2. hypocrisy: _____

3. jealousy: _____

4. arrogance: _____

5. honesty: _____

6 integrity: _____

7. revenge: _____

8. malice: _____

9. virtue: _____

10. prevarication: _____

11. avarice: _____

12. spite: _____

13. chicanery: _____

14. empathy: _____

15. mendacious: _____

16. haughty: _____

Mr. Wilson	Mr. Billson	Reverend Burgess
Barclay Goodson	the Stranger	Mary Richards
Edward Richards	Mr. Pinkerton	Mr. Titmarsh
Mrs. Titmarsh	the Reporter	Mr. Cox, the editor

25. The Man That Corrupted Hadleyburg

Short Answers

Write your answers to the questions below on the lines provided.

1. What do you think happened to the stranger the first time he was in Hadleyburg?

   _____

   _____

   _____

2. What do you think happened in Mark Twain's (the author's) life that inspired him to write such a story?

   _____

   _____

   _____

3. What do you think Reverend Burgess said in the sermon that got him fired?

   _____

   _____

   _____

4. What do you think Hadleyburg learned about itself from the experience with the bag of "gold"?

   _____

   _____

   _____

5. What do you think life was like in Hadleyburg after that fateful town meeting and the reading of the letters from the 19 prominent families?

   _____

   _____

   _____

25. The Man That Corrupted Hadleyburg

News Story

In the movie, a reporter circulated among the citizens, getting details of the incredible story about a man giving away forty thousand dollars. He interviewed prominent citizens of the town, including the Reverend Burgess.

Pretend you are that reporter and that you're from a famous newspaper, like the *Chicago Sun Times.* Write the story of the *day after* the town meeting. What was the mood in Hadleyburg? What happened to some people— Reverend Burgess, Edward and Mary Richards, and the other prominent families involved in the hoax? Quote some of the local citizens. What would they have said? What will the future of Hadleyburg be like?

Write the name of your paper across the top of the form below, then write the title of your article and your report.

25. The Man That Corrupted Hadleyburg

Answers

True or False

(1) + (2) + (3) 0 (4) + (5) + (6) + (7) + (8) + (9) + (10) 0 (11) 0 (12) +
(13) + (14) 0 (15) + (16) +

Vocabulary

1. envy: *desire for something that belongs to another*—Mr. Billson (or Wilson, Titmarsh)
2. hypocrisy: *pretending to be what one is not*—Mr. Pinkerton (or Wilson, Billson)
3. jealousy: *suspiciousness, protectiveness of what one has*—Mr. Wilson (or Billson, Pinkerton)
4. arrogance: *haughtiness, excessive pride*—Mrs. Titmarsh (or Wilson, Billson)
5. honesty: *truthfulness, fairness*—Reverend Burgess (or Goodson)
6. integrity: *honesty, incorruptibility*—Reverend Burgess (or Goodson)
7. revenge: *to inflict harm in return for an injury or insult*—the Stranger
8. malice: *desire to harm another, active ill will*—the Stranger (or Wilson, Billson)
9. virtue: *general moral excellence*—Reverend Burgess (or the Reporter?)
10. prevarication: *a lie*—Edward Richards (or Mary Richards, the Stranger, Pinkerton)
11. avarice: *greed for money*—Editor Cox (or Edward and Mary Richards, Wilson, Billson)
12. spite: *malice, or a grudge*—the Stranger
13. chicanery: *trickery*—the Stranger (or Billson, Wilson, the Richards, Pinkerton)
14. empathy: *emotional identification with another*—Reverend Burgess (toward Richards)
15. mendacious: *not truthful, lying*—Edward and Mary Richards (or Wilson, Billson, Pinkerton)
16. haughty: *having excessive pride in oneself and contempt for others*—Mrs. Titmarsh (or Billson, et al.)

Short Answers

Samples:
1. He was probably run out of town by the sheriff after being noticed by one of the prominent citizens as a vagrant and a drifter.
2. He probably entered a town when he was out of money and down on his luck, and his reception was not too friendly—the hotel owner wouldn't give him a room, etc.
3. He probably told the people to open up to others and quit criticizing those who don't dress, talk, or look like they do. They need more joy and less judgment in their lives.
4. That it was prone to "sinfulness" like any other town in the world. That Hadleyburg was not a paradise full of perfect people, as everyone had thought.
5. People probably smirked a lot as they did business at the various establishments in town run by the so-called "19'ers." And we could guess that some common people got elected to a few positions of responsibility in town.

News Story

Answers will vary.